# Teacher's Resource Masters

## Number and Operations in Base Ten

Daily Common Core Review

Reteaching

Practice

Enrichment



2-sided, stapled (22)

Foresman·Addison Wesley

# enVisionMATH®
## Common Core

PEARSON

Glenview, Illinois • Boston, Massachusetts • Chandler, Arizona • Upper Saddle River, New Jersey

PEARSON

ISBN-13: 978-0-328-68796-1
ISBN-10: 0-328-68796-0



4 5 6 7 8 9 10 V011 15 14 13 12

# Domain Number and Operations in Base Ten



Each lesson has a Teacher Resource Master for Daily Common Core Review, Reteaching, Practice and Enrichment.

Name ______________________



**1.** Eli's family eats $1\frac{3}{8}$ pizzas. Which drawing has $1\frac{3}{8}$ shaded?

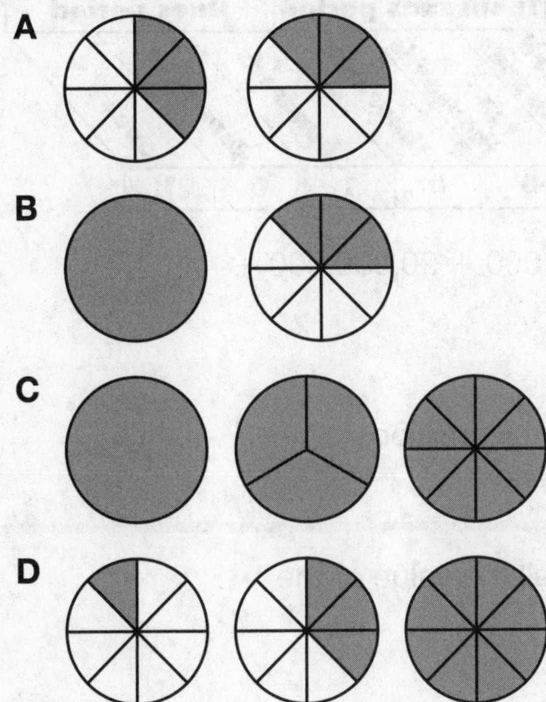


**2.** Barb has 2 cats. Rita has 13 fish and 1 dog. Sam has 4 dogs and 2 birds. How many animals do Barb, Rita, and Sam have all together?

**A** 31
**B** 22
**C** 19
**D** 12

**3.** Mr. Martin works 9 hours each day for 5 days. What is the total number of hours he works?

______________________

**4.** Jules tosses a penny 3 times. List all the possible combinations of heads (H) and tails (T) that Jules might get.

______________________

______________________

**5.** This drawing shows two streets that cross each other.

Oak Street
Main Street

When Main Street crosses Oak Street, what kind of angle do they appear to form?

______________________



 

Name ______________________



# Place Value

**Place-value chart:**

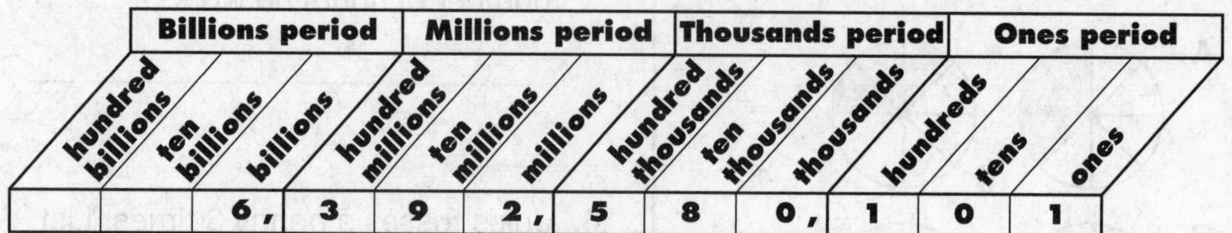


**Expanded form:** 6,000,000,000 + 300,000,000 + 90,000,000 + 2,000,000 + 500,000 + 80,000 + 100 + 1

**Standard form:** 6,392,580,101

**Word form:** six billion, three hundred ninety-two million, five hundred eighty thousand, one hundred one

Write the word name for each number and tell the value of the underlined digit.

1. 3,5<u>5</u>2,308,725

______________________

______________________

______________________

2. <u>8</u>43,208,732,833

______________________

______________________

______________________

______________________

3. Write 2,000,000,000 + 70,000,000 + 100,000 + 70,000 + 3,000 + 800 + 10 in standard form.

______________________

4. What number is 100,000,000 more than 5,438,724,022?

______________________



 

Name ______________________________

Practice
**1-1**

# Place Value

Write the word form for each number and tell the value of the underlined digit.

**1.** 34,23<u>5</u>,345

______________________________

______________________________

**2.** 1<u>9</u>,673,890,004

______________________________

______________________________

**3.** Write 2,430,090 in expanded form.

______________________________

Write each number in standard form.

**4.** 80,000,000 + 4,000,000 + 100 + 8 ____________

**5.** twenty-nine billion, thirty-two million ____________

**6.** What number is 10,000 less than 337,676? ____________

**7.** Which number is 164,502,423 decreased by 100,000?

**A** 164,402,423 **B** 164,501,423 **C** 164,512,423 **D** 264,502,423

**8.** Write 423,090,709,000 in word form.

______________________________

______________________________

______________________________



 

Name ______________________________

Enrichment
**1-1**

# Find the Numbers

Use the number chart to answer the questions. Circle each number you find. You can use only digits that are next to each other to make numbers. Read the rows from left to right. Read the columns from top to bottom.

COLUMNS

| ROWS | A | C | E | G | I | K | M | O | Q | S |
|---|---|---|---|---|---|---|---|---|---|---|
| B | 3 | 5 | 4 | 3 | 2 | 7 | 1 | 1 | 7 | 1 |
| D | 2 | 4 | 2 | 9 | 7 | 1 | 9 | 2 | 3 | 9 |
| F | 1 | 1 | 6 | 4 | 1 | 3 | 5 | 2 | 1 | 2 |
| H | 1 | 3 | 7 | 2 | 0 | 5 | 9 | 1 | 2 | 5 |
| J | 4 | 2 | 0 | 3 | 6 | 7 | 1 | 7 | 6 | 9 |
| L | 2 | 2 | 6 | 5 | 2 | 9 | 5 | 6 | 9 | 9 |
| N | 2 | 1 | 8 | 5 | 3 | 8 | 6 | 6 | 2 | 2 |
| P | 8 | 1 | 8 | 3 | 8 | 5 | 7 | 3 | 3 | 3 |
| R | 4 | 1 | 6 | 2 | 3 | 8 | 4 | 7 | 5 | 8 |
| T | 5 | 4 | 4 | 3 | 2 | 5 | 9 | 8 | 2 | 5 |

Write the letter of the

1. row that has the four-digit number with the least value. ______
2. column with the greatest number of digits in counting order. ______
3. column that has the three-digit number with the greatest value. ______
4. row with the palindrome with the greatest number of digits. (A palindrome is a number that is the same when read forward or backward. For example, the number 121 is a palindrome.) ______
5. column with the greatest number of odd numbers in counting order. ______
6. column with the palindrome with the greatest number of digits. ______
7. row with the greatest number of digits in reverse counting order. ______
8. column that has the five-digit number with the least value. ______



 

Name ______________________

Daily Common Core Review

**1-2**

**1.** A group of 36 students goes on a school field trip. Of all the students on the trip, 18 are in third grade. What is $\frac{18}{36}$ in simplest form?

**A** $\frac{1}{3}$

**B** $\frac{4}{12}$

**C** $\frac{8}{24}$

**D** $\frac{1}{2}$

**2.** Conor feeds his cats a total of 9 ounces of food each day. How many days will 414 ounces of food last?

**A** 21 days

**B** 27 days

**C** 46 days

**D** 49 days

**3.** In the year 2000, there were 1,631,192 Texans between 10 and 14 years old. What is the value of the digit in the ten-thousands place in 1,631,192?

**A** Ten thousand

**B** Sixty thousand

**C** Thirty thousand

**D** Ninety thousand

**4.** What fraction of these boxes are open? Write your answer in simplest form.

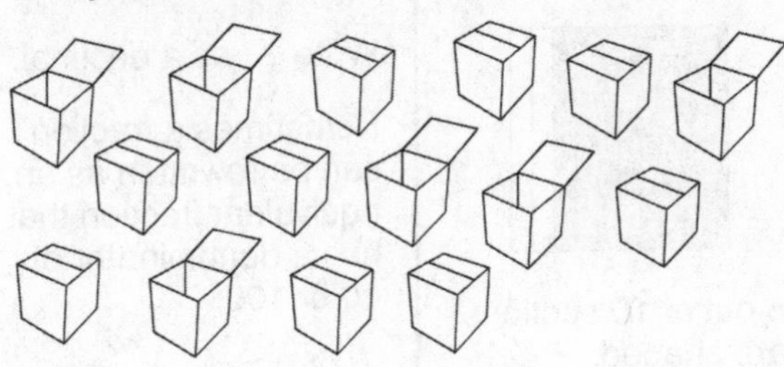

______________________

**5.** Mr. Lou gets 385 free minutes each month on his cell phone plan. How many free minutes does Mr. Lou get in 7 months?

______________________

**6.** The table shows the total cost of large packages of blank CDs.

| **Number of Packages** | 4 | 6 | 7 | 9 |
|---|---|---|---|---|
| **Total Cost** | \$44 | \$66 | \$77 | ? |

Describe how to find the cost of 9 large packages of blank CDs.

______________________

______________________



 

Name ______________________

# Tenths and Hundredths

Reteaching
**1-2**

Fractions can also be named using decimals.

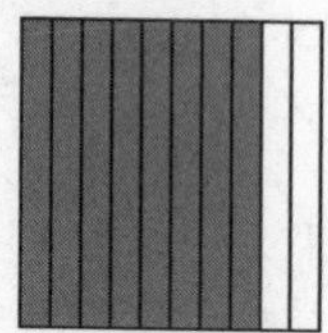

8 out of 10 sections are shaded.

The fraction is $\frac{8}{10}$.

The word name is eight tenths.

The decimal is 0.8.

Remember: the first place to the right of the decimal is tenths.

Write $\frac{2}{5}$ as a decimal.

Sometimes a fraction can be rewritten as an equivalent fraction that has a denominator of 10 or 100.

$\frac{2}{5} = \frac{2 \times 2}{5 \times 2} = \frac{4}{10}$

$\frac{4}{10} = 0.4$

So, $\frac{2}{5} = 0.4$.

Write $3\frac{3}{5}$ as a decimal.

First write the whole number.

3

Write the fraction as an equivalent fraction with a denominator of 10.

Change the fraction to a decimal.

$\frac{3}{5} = \frac{3 \times 2}{5 \times 2} = \frac{6}{10} = 0.6$

Write the decimal next to the whole number

3.6

So, $3\frac{3}{5} = 3.6$.

Write 0.07 as a fraction.

The word name for 0.07 is seven hundredths.

"Seven" is the numerator, and "hundredths" is the denominator.

So, $0.07 = \frac{7}{100}$.

Remember: the second place to the right of the decimal is hundredths.

Write each fraction or mixed number as a decimal.

**1.** $\frac{1}{5}$ ________ **2.** $\frac{6}{25}$ ________ **3.** $2\frac{3}{4}$ ________ **4.** $3\frac{9}{10}$ ________

Write each decimal as a fraction or mixed number.

**5.** 1.25 ________ **6.** 3.29 ________

**7.** 0.65 ________ **8.** 5.6 ________

**9.** Dan says $\frac{3}{5}$ is the same as 3.5. Is he correct? Explain.

______________________________________________

______________________________________________



 

Name ______________________________

Practice
1-2

# Tenths and Hundredths

Write a decimal and fraction for the shaded portion of each model.

**1.** 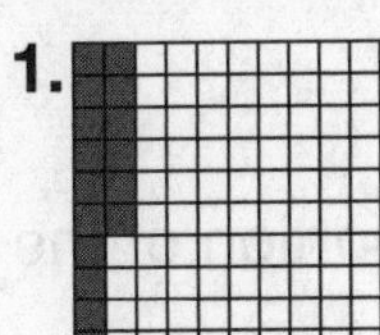

**2.** 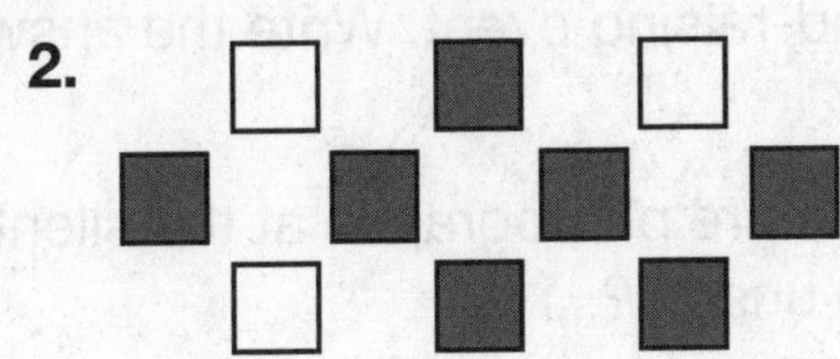

________ ________ ________ ________

Write each decimal as either a fraction or a mixed number.

**3.** 0.6 ________________ **4.** 0.73 ________________

**5.** 6.9 ________________ **6.** 8.57 ________________

Write each fraction or mixed number as a decimal.

**7.** $\frac{7}{10}$ ________________ **8.** $\frac{33}{100}$ ________________

**9.** $7\frac{2}{10}$ ________________ **10.** $3\frac{9}{100}$ ________________

Use division to change each fraction to a decimal.

**11.** $\frac{4}{5}$ ________________ **12.** $\frac{12}{25}$ ________________

**13.** $\frac{1}{50}$ ________________ **14.** $\frac{11}{20}$ ________________

**15.** When you convert 0.63 to a fraction, which of the following could be the first step of the process?

**A** Since there are 63 hundredths, multiply 0.63 and 100.

**B** Since there are 63 tenths, divide 0.63 by 10.

**C** Since there are 63 tenths, place 63 over 10.

**D** Since there are 63 hundredths, place 63 over 100.



 

Name ______________________________



# Dual Answers

You have volunteered to help raise money for your school's photography club by participating in various events. Read the description of each fund-raising event. Write the answer as both a fraction and a decimal.

1. You sold $\frac{4}{5}$ of the nature photographs at the silent auction. What portion of the photographs were unsold?

   ______________________________

2. After an hour at the snack table, you sold $\frac{1}{4}$ of the strawberry tarts. What portion of the tarts remain?

   ______________________________

3. Of the 100 donated gift baskets, you raffled off 97. What fraction of the baskets are left?

   ______________________________

4. The local camera shop contributed 10 antique cameras. The next day, you accepted bids for 4 of the cameras. What fraction of the total number of cameras is left to bid on?

   ______________________________

5. Students in the photography club agreed to take photos of people's pets. You started with 100 tickets and sold 83 the first week. What portion of the tickets remain?

   ______________________________



 

Name ______________________________



**1.** A swimmer wins a race by $\frac{2}{10}$ of a second. Which decimal is equal to $\frac{2}{10}$?

**A** 0.02
**B** 0.20
**C** 2.00
**D** 2.10

**2.** A baker uses $\frac{10}{4}$ cups of flour to make bread. Which decimal is equal to $\frac{10}{4}$?

**A** 4.1
**B** 2.5
**C** 2.2
**D** 0.4

**3.** What fraction of this tile floor is white?

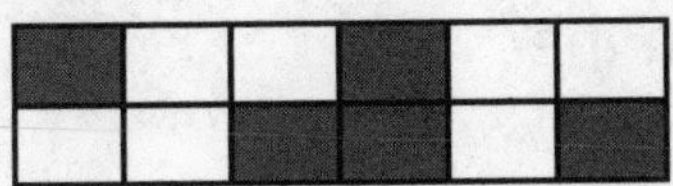

**A** $\frac{5}{12}$

**B** $\frac{12}{7}$

**C** $\frac{5}{7}$

**D** $\frac{7}{12}$

**4.** Marti's cat weighs 12.37 pounds. What is this weight written as a mixed number?

______________________________

**5.** The table shows the cost of adult admissions to a state park.

| **Number of Adults** | 4 | 5 | 7 | 9 |
|---|---|---|---|---|
| **Total Cost** | \$16 | \$20 | \$28 | ? |

What is the total cost for a group of 9 adults to go to the state park?

______________________________

**6.** What is the value of the underlined digit?

$34.\underline{2}05$

______________________________



 

Name ___________________________

# Thousandths

Reteaching
**1-3**

**Example 1:** Write 0.025 as a fraction.

| Ones | . | Tenths | Hundredths | Thousandths |
|---|---|---|---|---|
| 0 | . | 0 | 2 | 5 |

You can use a place-value chart to write a decimal as a fraction. Look at the place-value chart above. The place farthest to the right that contains a digit tells you the denominator of the fraction. In this case, it is thousandths. The number written in the place-value chart tells you the numerator of the fraction. Here, it is 25.

$0.025 = \frac{25}{1,000}$

**Example 2:** Write $\frac{11}{1,000}$ as a decimal.

| Ones | . | Tenths | Hundredths | Thousandths |
|---|---|---|---|---|
| | . | | | |

You can also use a place-value chart to write a fraction as a decimal. The denominator tells you the last decimal place in your number. Here, it is thousandths. The numerator tells you the decimal itself. Write a 1 in the hundredths place and a 1 in the thousandths place. Fill in the other places with a 0.

$\frac{11}{1,000} = 0.011$

Write each decimal as a fraction.

**1.** 0.002 ______

**2.** 0.037 ______

**3.** 0.099 ______

Write each fraction as a decimal.

**4.** $\frac{5}{1,000}$ ______

**5.** $\frac{76}{1,000}$ ______

**6.** $\frac{40}{1,000}$ ______

**7.** Matt reasoned that he can write $\frac{9}{1,000}$ as 0.9. Is he correct? Explain your answer.

______________________________

______________________________

______________________________



 

Name ______________________

Practice 1-3

# Thousandths

Write each decimal as either a fraction or a mixed number.

**1.** 0.007 ______________

**2.** 0.052 ______________

**3.** 0.038 ______________

**4.** 0.259 ______________

**5.** 3.020 ______________

**6.** 4.926 ______________

Write each fraction as a decimal.

**7.** $\frac{73}{1,000}$ ______________

**8.** $\frac{593}{1,000}$ ______________

**9.** $\frac{854}{1,000}$ ______________

**10.** $\frac{11}{1,000}$ ______________

**11.** $\frac{5}{1,000}$ ______________

**12.** $\frac{996}{1,000}$ ______________

Write the numbers in order from least to greatest.

**13.** $\frac{5}{1,000}$, 0.003, $\frac{9}{1,000}$ ______________

**14.** 0.021, 0.845, $\frac{99}{1,000}$ ______________

**15.** Look at the model at the right. Write a fraction and a decimal that the model represents.

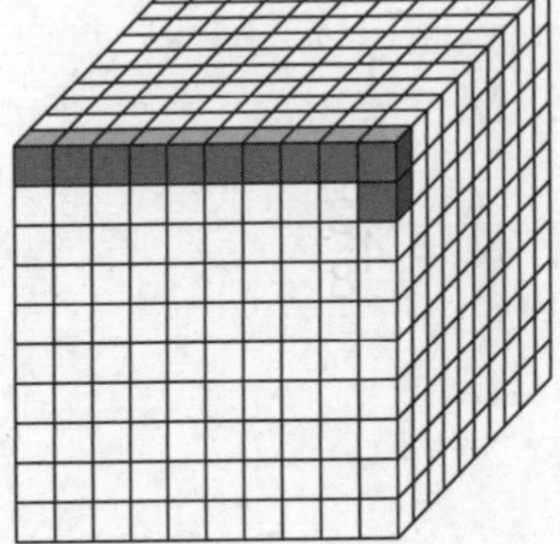

______________

**16.** In Tasha's school, 0.600 of the students participate in a school sport. If there are one thousand students in Tasha's school, how many participate in a school sport?

**A** 6,000 **B** 600 **C** 60 **D** 6

**17.** Explain how knowing that $5 \div 8 = 0.625$ helps you write the decimal for $4\frac{5}{8}$.

______________

______________



 

Name ______________________________



# Secret Code

Place the following points on the number line. Label the points with the letters to find the secret message.

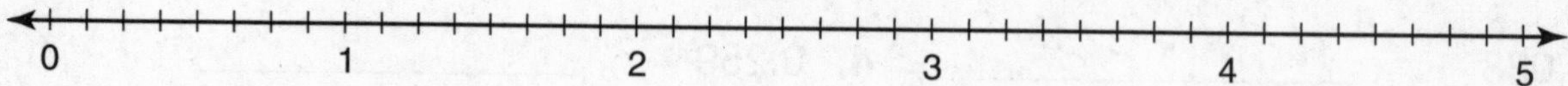


1. A = $\frac{1}{4}$
2. N = $2\frac{1}{8}$
3. E = $3\frac{7}{8}$
4. O = $4\frac{2}{8}$
5. E = $3\frac{5}{8}$
6. O = $2\frac{7}{8}$
7. E = $4\frac{1}{2}$
8. R = $2\frac{8}{8}$
9. F = $2\frac{3}{4}$
10. R = $\frac{4}{1}$
11. F = $1\frac{7}{8}$
12. S = $1\frac{1}{4}$
13. H = $\frac{1}{2}$
14. T = $\frac{3}{8}$
15. I = $1\frac{1}{8}$
16. U = $\frac{8}{4}$
17. M = $\frac{1}{8}$
18. V = $3\frac{3}{4}$
19. N = $4\frac{3}{8}$
20. Y = $4\frac{1}{8}$



 

Name ______________________________



**1.** Acme Nails made 55,672,459,257 nails last year. The Jones Company made <u>more</u> nails than Acme did. Which could be the number of nails made by the Jones Company?

**A** 55,599,599,399
**B** 55,674,348,146
**C** 55,573,560,458
**D** 55,672,360,368

**2.** The chart shows the distance to Star X from 4 other stars.

**Distance of Stars to Star X**

| Stars | Distance |
|---|---|
| P | 6,239,000,093 miles |
| Q | 6,340,999,122 miles |
| R | 6,239,100,291 miles |
| S | 6,308,512,300 miles |

Which lists the stars in order from least to greatest distance to Star X?

**A** P, R, S, Q
**B** P, Q, R, S
**C** S, R, Q, P
**D** S, P, Q, R

**3.** Write a number that is less than 4,001,020,000.

______________________________

______________________________

______________________________

**4.** Write a number that is greater than 10,910,099,999, but is less than 11,000,000,000.

______________________________

______________________________

______________________________

______________________________

______________________________

______________________________

**5.** Look at the shape below.

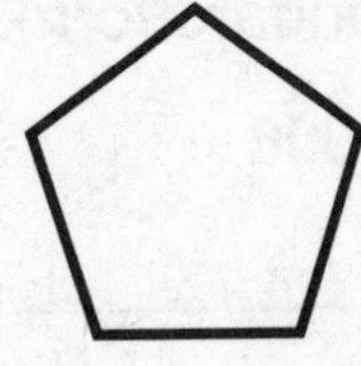

How many vertices does this shape have?

______________________________



 

Name ______________________

Reteaching **1-4**

# Decimal Place Value

Here are different ways to represent 2.753.

**Place-value chart:**

| Ones | | Tenths | Hundredths | Thousandths |
|---|---|---|---|---|
| 2 | . | 7 | 5 | 3 |

**Expanded Form:**

2 + 0.7 + 0.05 + 0.003

**Standard form:** 2.753

**Word Form:** Two and seven hundred fifty-three thousandths

Complete the place-value chart for the following number. Write its word form and tell the value of the underlined digit.

**1.** 6.3<u>2</u>4

| Ones | | Tenths | Hundredths | Thousandths |
|---|---|---|---|---|
| | . | | | |

______________________

______________________

______________________

Write each number in standard form.

**2.** 5 + 0.1 + 0.03 + 0.006

______________________

**3.** Two and seven hundred twenty-four thousandths

______________________



 

Name ______________________

Practice
**1-4**

# Decimal Pl

Write the word form o e
underlined digit.

**1.** 3.100

______________________

**2.** 5.267

______________________

**3.** 2.778

______________________

Write each number in standard form.

**4.** 8 + 0.0 + 0.05 + 0.009

______________________

**5.** 1 + 0.9 + 0.08 + 0.001

______________________

Write two decimals that are equivalent to the given decimal.

**6.** 5.300 ______________

**7.** 3.7 ______________

**8.** 0.9 ______________

**9.** The longest stem on Eli's geranium plant is 7.24 inches. Write 7.24 in word form.

______________________

______________________

**10.** The number 4.124 has two 4s. Why does each 4 have a different value?

______________________

______________________

______________________



 

Name ______________________________



# What Is the Decimal?

Use the clues to identify each number. Write each number in word form, expanded form, and standard form.

1. This number is the same as thirty-one and eight hundred eighty thousandths.

2. This number is 500 thousandths less than 2.845.

3. This number is 0.02 more than five and five tenths.

4. This number is equivalent to seventeen and fifty thousandths.

5. This number is three tenths less than twenty-four and twenty hundredths.

6. This number is the same as sixty-eight and 830 thousandths.



 

Name ______________________________

Daily Common Core Review
**1-5**

**1.** What is the value of the underlined digit?

1.20<u>7</u>

**A** 0.007
**B** 0.7
**C** 2.07
**D** 2.7

**2.** Caroline has five and six hundred twenty thousandths yards of batting to put into a quilt. What is that number in standard form?

**A** 5,620
**B** 5,600.20
**C** 5.620
**D** 0.5620

**3.** 27,563 is greater than ______?

**A** 27,536
**B** 27,563
**C** 27,567
**D** 27,653

**4.** Nico's new skateboard is 7.75 inches wide. Write 7.75 in word form.

______________________________

**5.** Name two decimals that are equivalent to 7.75.

______________________________

______________________________

**6.** Kari measures thirty-eight and ninety seven hundredths kilograms. What is her mass in standard form?

______________________________

**7.** What is the value of the digit 9 in the number that shows Kari's mass?

______________________________



 

Name ______________________

Reteaching
**1-5**

# Comparing and Ordering Decimals

List the numbers in order from least to greatest:

6.943, 5.229, 6.825, 6.852, 6.779

**Step 1: Write the numbers, lining up places. Begin at the left to find the greatest or least number.**

6.943
5.229
6.825
6.852
6.779

5.229 is the least.

**Step 2: Write the remaining numbers, lining up places. Find the greatest and least. Order the other numbers.**

6.943 ← greatest
6.825 → 6.825
6.852 → 6.852
6.779 ← least

6.779 is the least.
6.943 is the greatest.
6.852 is greater than 6.825.

**Step 3: Write the numbers from least to greatest.**

5.229
6.779
6.825
6.852
6.943

Complete. Write >, <, or = for each ◯.

**1.** 7.539 ◯ 7.344 **2.** 9.202 ◯ 9.209 **3.** 0.75 ◯ 0.750

Order these numbers from least to greatest.

**4.** 3.898 3.827 3.779

______________________

**5.** 5.234 5.199 5.002 5.243

______________________

Which had the faster speed?

**6.** Driver A or Driver D

______________________

**7.** Driver C or Driver A

______________________

**Car Racing Winners**

| Driver | Average Speed (mph) |
|---|---|
| Driver A | 145.155 |
| Driver B | 145.827 |
| Driver C | 147.956 |
| Driver D | 144.809 |



 

Name ______________________________



# Comparing and Ordering Decimals

Write >, <, or = for each ◯.

**1.** 5.424 ◯ 5.343 **2.** 0.33 ◯ 0.330 **3.** 9.489 ◯ 9.479

**4.** 21.012 ◯ 21.01 **5.** 223.21 ◯ 223.199 **6.** 5.43 ◯ 5.432

Order these numbers from least to greatest.

**7.** 8.37, 8.3, 8.219, 8.129 ______________________________

**8.** 0.012, 0.100, 0.001, 0.101 ______________________________

**9.** Name three numbers between 0.33 and 0.34.

______________________________

**10.** Which runner came in first place?

______________________________

**11.** Who ran faster, Amanda or Steve?

______________________________

**12.** Who ran for the longest time?

______________________________

**Half-Mile Run**

| Runner | Time (minutes) |
|---|---|
| Amanda | 8.016 |
| Calvin | 7.049 |
| Liz | 7.03 |
| Steve | 8.16 |

**13.** Which number is less than 28.43?

**A** 28.435 **B** 28.34 **C** 28.430 **D** 29.43

**14.** Explain why it is not reasonable to say that 4.23 is less than 4.13.

______________________________

______________________________

______________________________



 

Name ______________________________



# Digit Detection

Use each digit only once to make the comparisons true.

1. Use 2, 3, and 4.
   □.□6 < 2.□2

2. Use 7 and 8.
   7.2□ > □.23

3. Use 0, 3, and 5.
   □.4□7 < 0.45□

4. Use 4 and 6.
   57.□64 > 57.46□

5. Use 1, 3, and 9.
   9.3□ < 9.□3 < □.34

6. Use 3, 6, and 9.
   □.138 > 8.□87 > 8.3□5

7. Use 6, 3, 4, and 1.
   5.4□□ > □.34 > 4.□2

8. Use 6, 0, 9, and 5.
   6.□□ < □.08 < 6.0□

Fill in the boxes to make the comparison true. List 5 possible combinations.

9. Use 7, 8, and 9.

   36.□4 < 3□.□4

   36.□4 < 3□.□4

   36.□4 < 3□.□4

   36.□4 < 3□.□4

   36.□4 < 3□.□4

10. Use 3, 2, 1, and 0.

    □.□68 > 2.□4□

    □.□68 > 2.□4□

    □.□68 > 2.□4□

    □.□68 > 2.□4□

    □.□68 > 2.□4□



 

Name ___________________________________________

Daily Common Core Review

**1-6**

**1.** The chart shows about how much one U.S. dollar was worth in euros, the currency used in Europe.

**Worth of U.S. Dollar in Euros**

| Date | Estimated Worth of $1 in Euros |
|---|---|
| January 17 | 0.828 |
| February 17 | 0.834 |
| March 17 | 0.820 |
| April 17 | 0.815 |

On which date was a U.S. dollar worth the most amount in euros?

**A** January 17

**B** February 17

**C** March 17

**D** April 17

**2.** The speeds in pages per minute (ppm) for four printers are: 7.105 ppm, 7.221 ppm, 7.4 ppm, and 7.08 ppm. Which lists the speeds in order from greatest to least number of pages per minute?

**A** 7.08, 7.105, 7.221, 7.4

**B** 7.4, 7.221, 7.105, 7.08

**C** 7.221, 7.105, 7.08, 7.4

**D** 7.4, 7.08, 7.105, 7.221

**3.** Fill in the blanks with the digits 3, 4, and 5 to write the greatest possible decimal. Use each digit once.

0 . ___ ___ ___

**4.** Look at the number line below.

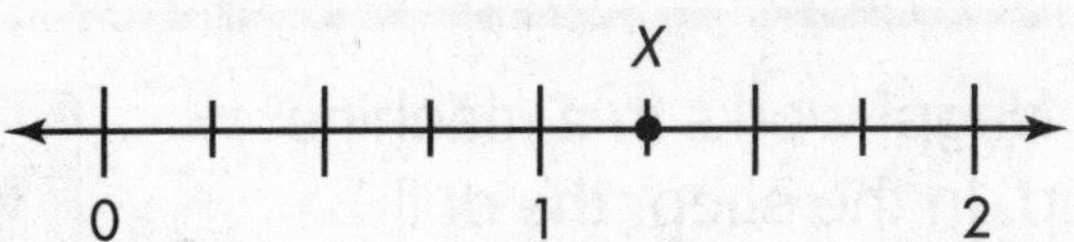


What value does point *X* show?

___________________________________

**5.** Fill in the blanks with the digits 0, 1, 2, and 3 to make each number sentence true. Use each digit once in each number sentence.

**a.** ___ . ___ ___ ___ > 2.099

**b.** ___ . ___ ___ ___ < 2.099



 

Name ______________________________



# Problem Solving: Look for a Pattern

Mr. Nagpi works in a machine shop. In the shop, the drill bits are kept in a cabinet with drawers. The drawers are marked with the diameter of the bits as shown on the right. Some of the labels are missing. Help Mr. Nagpi complete the drawer labels.

**Drill Bits**

| | | | | |
|---|---|---|---|---|
| 0.10 in. | 0.12 in. | 0.14 in. | 0.16 in. | 0.18 in. |
| 0.20 in. | 0.22 in. | 0.24 in. | 0.26 in. | 0.28 in. |
| 0.30 in. | 0.32 in. | 0.34 in. | | |

**Read and Understand**

What do you know?

Some drawers are labeled with decimals.

What are you trying to find?

A way to find the values of the missing labels

**Plan and Solve**

**Find a pattern for the decimals.**

1. Look for a pattern to the change in the tenth-values across a row or down a column.

   1. The tenth-values are not increasing across a row. They are increasing by 1 down a column.

2. Look for a pattern to the change in the hundredth-values across a row or down a column.

   2. The hundredth-values are increasing by 2 across a row. They are not increasing down a column.

3. Use the patterns to complete the table.

   3. The missing labels in the third row are 0.36 in. and 0.38 in.

Find the pattern in the table. Then fill in the missing values in the table.

| | | | | |
|---|---|---|---|---|
| 0.20 | 0.21 | 0.22 | 0.23 | 0.24 |
| 0.50 | 0.51 | 0.52 | 0.53 | |
| 0.80 | 0.81 | 0.82 | | |



 

Name ______________________________

Practice
**1-6**

# Problem Solving: Look for a Pattern

Determine the pattern and then complete the grids.

**1.**

| 0.87 | | 0.89 | |
|---|---|---|---|

**2.**

| 0.12 |
|---|
| 0.22 |
| |

**3.**

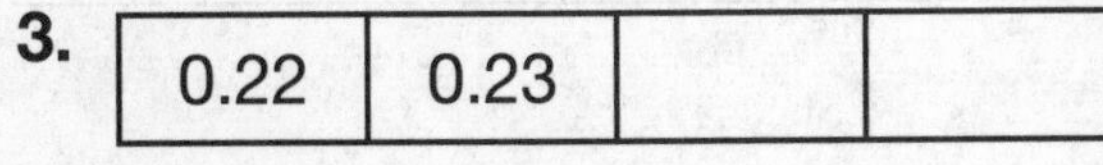

| 0.22 | 0.23 | | |
|---|---|---|---|

**4.**

| 0.56 |
|---|
| |
| 0.76 |

**5.** In a list of numbers, the pattern increases by 0.001 as you move to the right. If the third number in the list is 0.064, what is the first number in the list? Explain how you know.

______________________________

______________________________

**6.** If 5 school buses arrive, each carrying exactly 42 passengers, which expression would you use to show how many people in all arrived on the school buses?

**A** $42 + 5$ **B** $42 - 5$ **C** $42 \times 5$ **D** $42 \div 5$

**7.** Mishell arranged her coins in the following pattern: \$0.27, \$0.29, \$0.31, \$0.33. Explain what her pattern is, and then tell what the next amount of coins would be.

______________________________

______________________________


 

Name ______________________________



# Gridlock!

**1.** Describe a pattern you could use to complete the following grid, and then complete it.

| 0.35 | | |
|---|---|---|
| | | |
| | | 0.95 |

______________________________________________

______________________________________________

______________________________________________

**2.** Describe a pattern you could use to complete the following grid, and then complete it.

| 0.22 | | |
|---|---|---|
| | | |
| | | 0.84 |

______________________________________________

______________________________________________

______________________________________________

**3.** What is the missing number in the grid?

| | 0.33 | 0.35 | 0.37 |
|---|---|---|---|

**4.** Doug drew a grid of seven cells in a row. The pattern was: hundredths increase by 1 as you move to the right. The number 0.90 was in the middle cell. What did Doug's grid look like?



 

Name ____________________

Daily Common Core Review

**2-1**

**1.** The table shows the price of a hot dog at the school fair for the past 4 years.

**Price of Hot Dogs**

| **Year** | 2001 | 2002 | 2003 | 2004 |
|---|---|---|---|---|
| **Price** | $0.90 | $0.91 | $0.92 | |

Which was most likely the price of a hot dog at the school fair in 2004?

**A** $0.92
**B** $0.93
**C** $0.95
**D** $0.99

**2.** The table shows the thickness of four kinds of paper.

**Paper Thicknesses**

| **Kind of Paper** | **Thickness (in millimeters)** |
|---|---|
| Book | 0.147 |
| Cover | 0.152 |
| Index | 0.216 |
| Rag | 0.081 |

Which lists the kinds of paper in order from thinnest to thickest?

**A** Book, Cover, Index, Rag
**B** Book, Cover, Rag, Index
**C** Rag, Cover, Index, Book
**D** Rag, Book, Cover, Index

**3.** Fill the boxes in the decimal grid below. Use the pattern *add 0.001*.

| 0.345 | | | |
|---|---|---|---|

**4.** The graph shows the number of students in the lunchroom wearing different kinds of shoes.

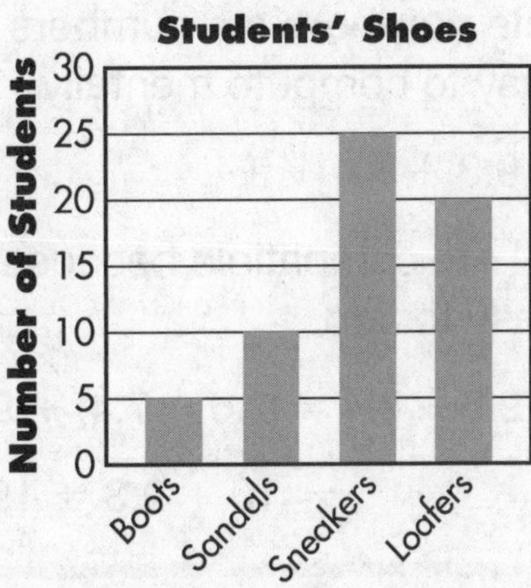


Which kind of shoes are the most popular?

____________________



 

Name ____________________

Reteaching **2-1**

# Mental Math

There are several ways that you can add and subtract decimals mentally to solve a problem.

**Commutative Property of Addition**

You can add two decimal numbers in any order.

$15.75 + 2.25 = 2.25 + 15.75$

**Compatible numbers** are numbers that are easy to compute mentally.

$2.6 + 9.3 + 7.4$

2.6 and 7.4 are compatible because they are easy to add.

$2.6 + 9.3 + 7.4 = (2.6 + 7.4) + 9.3$
$= 10 + 9.3 = 19.3$

**Associative Property of Addition**

You can change the groupings of addends.

$1.7 + (1.3 + 7) = (1.7 + 1.3) + 7$

With **compensation**, you adjust one or both decimal numbers to make computations easier and compensate to get the final answer.

$$\begin{array}{l} 3.76 - 1.26 \\ -.01 \quad -\ .01 \\ \downarrow \qquad\quad \downarrow \\ 3.75 - 1.25 = 2.5 \end{array}$$

Add or subtract mentally.

1. $16.9 + 12.1 =$ ________
2. $100.5 - 21.5 =$ ________
3. $8.01 + 1.09 =$ ________
4. $2.65 + 4.01 + 3.34 =$ ________
5. How much heavier is a Hippo than a Moose?

________________________

6. How heavy are the Elephant and the Rhino combined?

________________________

7. What is the total weight of all four animals?

________________________

**Weight of Zoo Animals**

| Animal | Weight (Tons) |
|---|---|
| Hippo | 2.5 |
| Elephant | 3.85 |
| Rhino | 2.15 |
| Moose | .5 |



 

Name ____________________

# Mental Math

Show how you can use mental math to add or subtract.

**1.** 7.03 + 9.0 + 3.07 = ________ **2.** 63.75 − 13.25 = ________

**Estimated Population in Millions**

| City | State | Population |
|---|---|---|
| San Antonio | Texas | 1.4 million |
| Phoenix | Arizona | 1.6 million |
| San Diego | California | 1.3 million |
| Chicago | Illinois | 2.7 million |

**3.** How many more people live in Phoenix than live in San Antonio? ________

**4.** How many people live in San Diego and Chicago combined? ________

**5.** A hotel bought 56.4 lb of apples in August from a local orchard. In September, the hotel purchased an additional 52.34 lb of apples and 32.26 lb of strawberries. How many pounds of fruit did the hotel buy?

**A** 132 lbs **B** 141 lbs **C** 139 lbs **D** 140.5 lbs

**6.** **Explain It** Write the definition and give an example of the Commutative Property of Addition using decimal numbers.

________________________________________

________________________________________

________________________________________



 

Name ______________________________

# Puzzle Squares



In a puzzle square, the sum of all the numbers in any row, column, or along any diagonal is the same. In the square at the right, every row, column, and diagonal has a sum of 18.

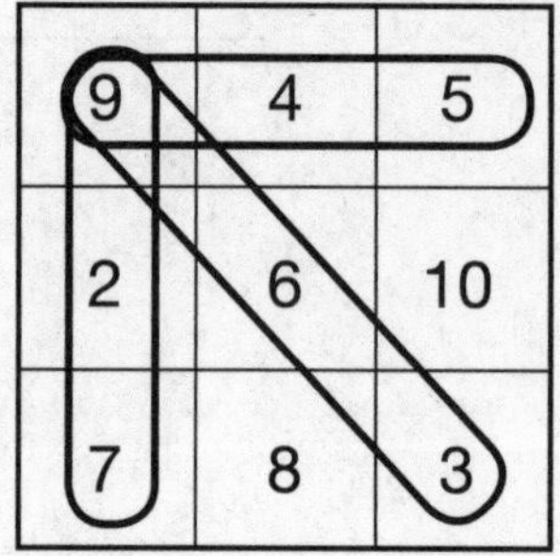


Write the missing number in each puzzle square.

**1.**

| | | |
|---|---|---|
| 6 | | 10 |
| 11 | 7 | 3 |
| 4 | 9 | 8 |

**2.**

| | | |
|---|---|---|
| 14 | 9 | 16 |
| 15 | | 11 |
| 10 | 17 | 12 |

Look at each number square. Circle the one that is a puzzle square.

**3.**

| | | |
|---|---|---|
| 3 | 13 | 11 |
| 7 | 5 | 15 |
| 17 | 9 | 1 |

| | | |
|---|---|---|
| 5 | 8 | 2 |
| 10 | 6 | 9 |
| 3 | 4 | 7 |

| | | |
|---|---|---|
| 11 | 6 | 13 |
| 12 | 10 | 8 |
| 7 | 14 | 9 |

Make your own puzzle squares.

**4.**

| | | |
|---|---|---|
| | | |
| | 5 | |
| | | |

**5.**

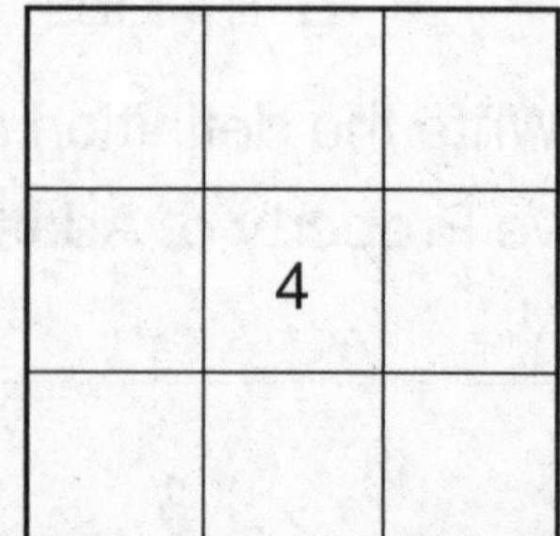




 

Name ______________________



**1.** The chart shows the growth of a plant each month.

**Monthly Plant Growth**

| Month | Growth (in millimeters) |
|---|---|
| May | 3 |
| June | 16 |
| July | 27 |

What is the total growth of the plant from May through July?

**A** 46 millimeters

**B** 30 millimeters

**C** 27 millimeters

**D** 24 millimeters

**2. Mental Math** Jenny read 47 pages last week. This week she read 102 pages. How many more pages did Jenny read this week than last week?

**A** 53

**B** 55

**C** 102

**D** 149

**3.** Rico buys a rectangular rug to put on his living room floor. The rug is 8 feet long and 6 feet wide. What is the area of the floor that the rug will cover?

______________________

**4.** Kim has $260 in her checking account. She puts in $39. Then she writes a check for $58. How much is left in Kim's account?

______________________

**5.** What is the value of the underlined digit?
8,531,980,112

______________________



 

Name ______________________________



# Rounding Whole Numbers and Decimals

You can use the number line below to help you round 8,237,650 to the nearest million. Is 8,237,650 closer to 8,000,000 or 9,000,000?

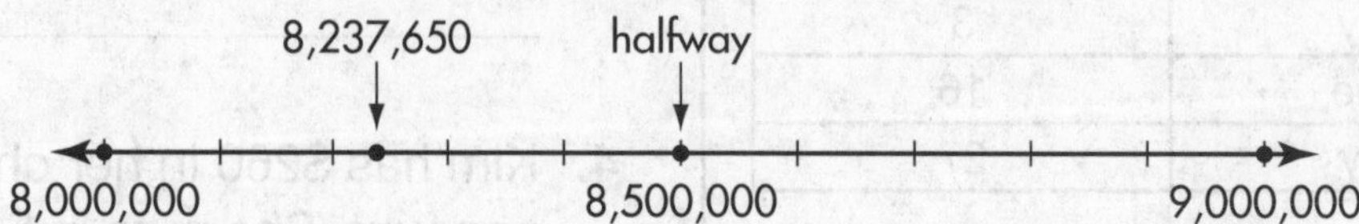


8,237,650 is less than halfway to 9,000,000. 8,237,650 is closer to 8,000,000.

The number line can also help you round 7.762 to the nearest tenth. Is 7.762 closer to 7.7 or 7.8?

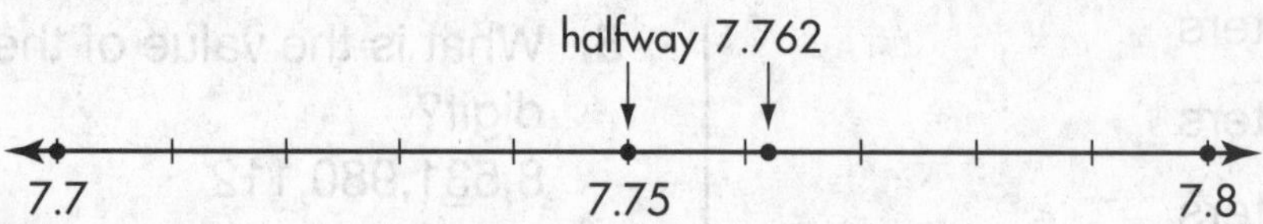


7.762 is more than halfway to 7.8. 7.762 is closer to 7.8.

Round each number to the place of the underlined digit.

**1.** 4,<u>7</u>25,806 ______________________

**2.** <u>7</u>.049 ______________________

**3.** <u>1</u>65,023,912 ______________________

**4.** 18.<u>6</u>92 ______________________

**5.** Round the number of connected computers in Year 2 to the nearest ten million.

______________________

**Number of Computers Connected to the Internet**

| | |
|---|---|
| Year 1 | 30,979,376 |
| Year 2 | 42,199,279 |
| Year 3 | 63,592,854 |

**6.** Marc earned $9.37 per hour working at the library. Round his wage to the nearest ten cents.

______________________



 

Name ______________________

Practice
2-2

# Rounding Whole Numbers and Decimals

Round each number to the place of the underlined digit.

**1.** 32.<u>6</u>0 ______________

**2.** 48<u>9</u>,334,209 ______________

**3.** 32<u>4</u>,650 ______________

**4.** 32.<u>0</u>73 ______________

**5.** Name two different numbers that round to 30 when rounded to the nearest ten.

______________________________

In 2000, Italy produced 7,464,000 tons of wheat, and Pakistan produced 21,079,000 tons of wheat. Round each country's wheat production in tons to the nearest hundred thousand.

**6.** Italy ______________

**7.** Pakistan ______________

The price of wheat in 1997 was $3.38 per bushel. In 1998, the price was $2.65 per bushel. Round the price per bushel of wheat for each year to the nearest tenth of a dollar.

**8.** 1997 ______________

**9.** 1998 ______________

**10.** Which number rounds to 15,700,000 when rounded to the nearest hundred thousand?

**A** 15,000,000 **B** 15,579,999 **C** 15,649,999 **D** 15,659,999

**11.** **Writing to Explain** Write a definition of rounding in your own words.

______________________________

______________________________



 

Name ______________________



# Census Rounding

The table shows July 2005 population estimates for the five fastest-growing U.S. cities over the course of a year.

| Rank | Geographic Area | Population Estimate |
|---|---|---|
| 1 | Elk Grove, CA | 112,338 |
| 2 | North Las Vegas, NV | 176,635 |
| 3 | Port St. Lucie, FL | 131,692 |
| 4 | Gilbert, AZ | 173,989 |
| 5 | Cape Coral, FL | 140,010 |

**1.** Round the population of each city to the nearest thousand in the table below.

| | |
|---|---|
| Elk Grove, CA | |
| North Las Vegas, NV | |
| Port St. Lucie, FL | |
| Gilbert, AZ | |
| Cape Coral, FL | |

**2.** Round the population of each city to the nearest ten thousand in the table below.

| | |
|---|---|
| Elk Grove, CA | |
| North Las Vegas, NV | |
| Port St. Lucie, FL | |
| Gilbert, AZ | |
| Cape Coral, FL | |



 

Name ____________________

Daily Common Core Review

**2-3**

1. Ms. Alvarez's class collects 54 pounds of food during their holiday food drive. Which number sentence could you use to find how many 6-pound bags of food the students can give away?

   **A** $54 + 6 = \square$

   **B** $54 - 6 = \square$

   **C** $54 \times 6 = \square$

   **D** $54 \div 6 = \square$

2. The driving time between Houston and Los Angeles is about 22.88 hours. What is this number rounded to the nearest tenth?

   **A** 20

   **B** 22.88

   **C** 22.9

   **D** 23.0

3. Last year, the Able Company made less money than the Baker Company. Baker made $35,021,242,010. Which could be the amount of money Able made?

   **A** $35,102,831,009

   **B** $35,019,300,020

   **C** $35,030,000,105

   **D** $35,130,241,000

4. As of June 19, 2006, the population of the earth was estimated at 6,523,183,959. What is this number rounded to the nearest hundred million?

   ____________________

5. What is the number below rounded to the place of the underlined digit?

   58<u>2</u>.091

   ____________________

6. Write 4,508,020,993 in word form.

   ____________________

   ____________________

   ____________________

   ____________________

   ____________________

   ____________________



 

Name ______________________________

Reteaching
**2-3**

# Estimating Sums and Differences

During one week, Mr. Graham drove a truck to five different towns to make deliveries. Estimate how far he drove in all.

**Mr. Graham's Mileage Log**

| Cities | Mileage |
|---|---|
| Mansley to Mt. Hazel | 243 |
| Mt. Hazel to Perkins | 303 |
| Perkins to Alberton | 279 |
| Alberton to Fort Maynard | 277 |
| Fort Maynard to Mansley | 352 |

To estimate the sum, you can round each number to the nearest hundred miles.

$$\begin{array}{rcr} 243 & \Rightarrow & 200 \\ 303 & \Rightarrow & 300 \\ 279 & \Rightarrow & 300 \\ 277 & \Rightarrow & 300 \\ \underline{+352} & \Rightarrow & \underline{+400} \\ & & 1{,}500 \text{ mi} \end{array}$$

Mr. Graham drove about 1,500 mi.

You can estimate differences in a similar way.

Estimate 7.25 − 4.98.

You can round each number to the nearest whole number.

$$\begin{array}{rcr} 7.25 & \Rightarrow & 7 \\ \underline{-4.98} & \Rightarrow & \underline{-5} \\ & & 2 \end{array}$$

The difference is about 2.

Estimate each sum or difference.

**1.** 19.7 − 6.9 ______________________

**2.** 59 + 43 + 95 ______________________

**3.** 582 + 169 + 23 ______________________

**4.** 87.99 − 52.46 ______________________

**5.** **Estimation** Brigid worked 16.75 h. Kevin worked 12.50 h. About how many more hours did Brigid work than Kevin?

______________________


 

Name ______________________________

Practice
**2-3**

# Estimating Sums and Differences

Estimate each sum or difference.

**1.** 5,602 − 2,344 ____________ **2.** 7.4 + 3.1 + 9.8 ____________

**3.** 2,314 + 671 ____________ **4.** 54.23 − 2.39 ____________

**5.** Wesley estimated 5.82 − 4.21 to be about 2. Is this an overestimate or an underestimate? Explain.

______________________________

______________________________

**6.** Estimate the total precipitation in inches and the total number of days with precipitation for Asheville and Wichita.

**Average Yearly Precipitation of U.S. Cities**

| City | Inches | Days |
|---|---|---|
| Asheville, North Carolina | 47.71 | 124 |
| Wichita, Kansas | 28.61 | 85 |

______________________________

**7.** Which numbers should you add to estimate the answer to this problem: 87,087 + 98,000?

**A** 88,000 + 98,000

**B** 85,000 + 95,000

**C** 87,000 + 98,000

**D** 80,000 + 90,000

**8. Estimation** Estimate the total weight of two boxes that weigh 9.4 lb and 62.6 lb using rounding and compatible numbers. Which estimate is closer to the actual total weight? Why?

______________________________

______________________________

______________________________



 

Name ____________________

Enrichment **2-3**

# A Good Cause

The Canine War Heroes group needs to raise $700 for a statue honoring dogs that served in the military. The group must choose one of the following fundraising events.

**A.** The Agility Club held a fun trial. Each ticket for a dog to run through the obstacle course cost $4.00, and the club sold 147 tickets. The expenses were $92.00.

**B.** The Jr. Canine Club sold dog cookie jars. The large cookie jars sold for $7.75 each, the medium cookie jars sold for $6.25 each, and the small cookie jars sold for $5.50 each. The club sold 29 large cookie jars, 35 medium cookie jars, and 44 small cookie jars. The expenses were $143.00.

**C.** The Veterans' Club washed dogs to raise money. The club charged $15 to wash each dog and washed 42 dogs. The expenses were $109.00.

**1.** About how much did each fundraising event earn (before expenses)?

Choice A ________ Choice B ________ Choice C ________

**2.** Estimate how much each fundraising event will earn after expenses.

Choice A ________ Choice B ________ Choice C ________

**3.** Based on the three fundraising events, which would you suggest the Canine War Heroes group choose? Explain.

____________________

____________________

____________________

**4.** If the group wants to choose two of the fundraising events, how many possible combinations are there? List the combinations.

____________________

____________________

Name ______________________



**1.** A special electric car has a small engine that charges the battery on the go if it falls below $\frac{3}{10}$ of its capacity. Which of the following is less than $\frac{3}{10}$?

**A** $\frac{1}{5}$

**B** $\frac{2}{6}$

**C** $\frac{3}{5}$

**D** $\frac{4}{8}$

**2.** Write the missing information in the table below.

| | |
|---|---|
| $16 \times 1 =$ | 16 |
| $16 \times 10 =$ | 160 |
| $16 \times 100 =$ | |
| $16 \times 1{,}000 =$ | 16,000 |

**3.** What decimal is represented by the shaded part of the grid?

**A** 0.13

**B** 0.67

**C** 0.73

**D** 0.87

**4.** There are 76 people signed up for a speedboat tour. Each speedboat can transport 9 people. How many speedboats will be needed to transport all of the people who signed up?

______________________

**5.** Jake wants to estimate 15.92 + 0.85. How can he use rounding to estimate the sum? What is the estimate?

______________________

______________________

______________________

______________________

______________________

______________________

______________________



 

Name ______________________________



# Modeling Addition and Subtraction of Decimals

## Adding decimals using a hundredths grid:

Add 0.32 + 0.17.

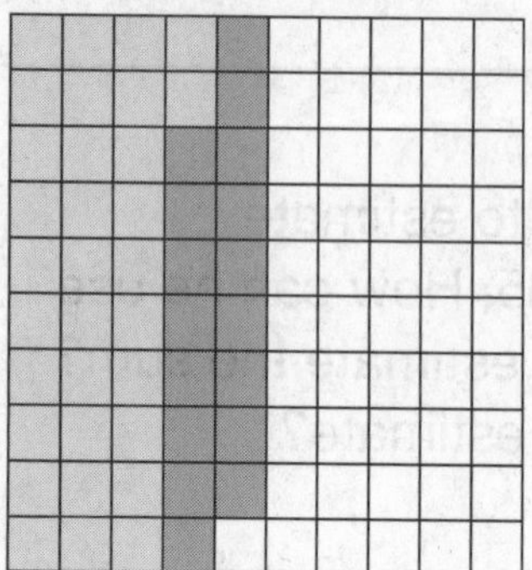

**Step 1:** Shade 32 squares to show 0.32.

**Step 2:** Use a different color. Shade 17 squares to show 0.17.

**Step 3:** Count all the squares that are shaded. How many hundredths are shaded in all? Write the decimal for the total shaded squares: 0.49.

So, 0.32 + 0.17 = 0.49.

## Subtracting decimals using a hundredths grid:

Subtract 0.61 − 0.42.

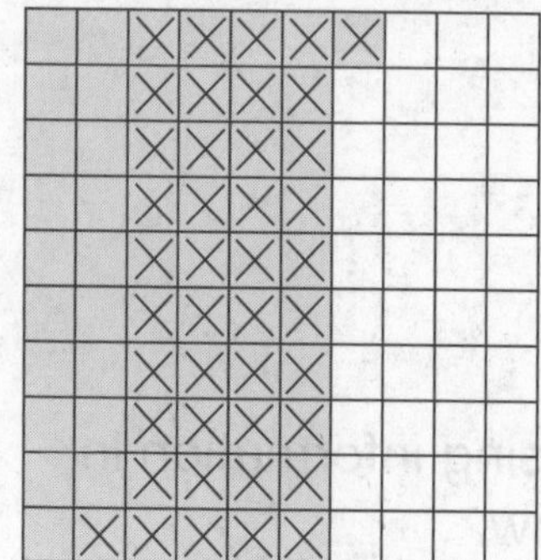

**Step 1:** Shade 61 squares to show 0.61.

**Step 2:** Cross out 42 squares to show 0.42.

**Step 3:** Count the squares that are shaded but not crossed out. Write the decimal: 0.19.

So, 0.61 − 0.42 = 0.19.

Add or subtract. You may use hundredths grids to help.

1. 0.22 + 0.35 = __________

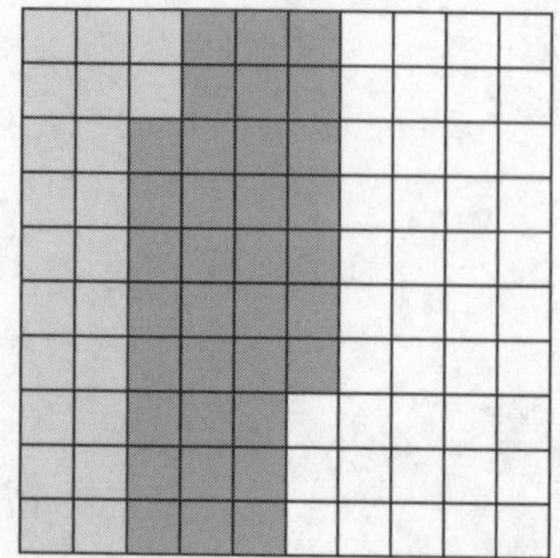

2. 0.52 − 0.41 = __________

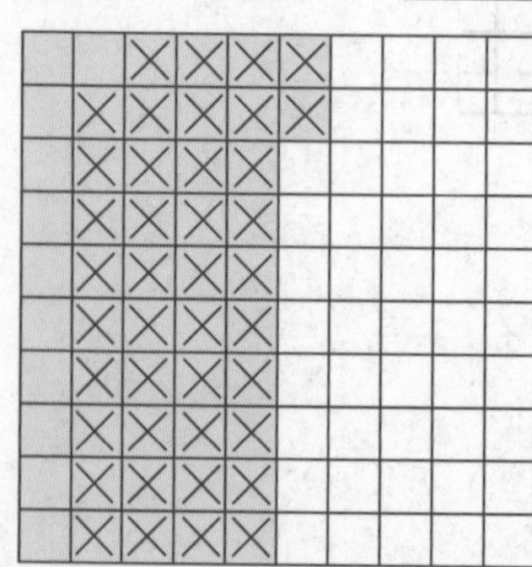



 

Name ______________________



# Modeling Addition and Subtraction of Decimals

Add or subtract. Use hundredths grids if necessary.

**1.** 0.12 + 0.56 = ________ 

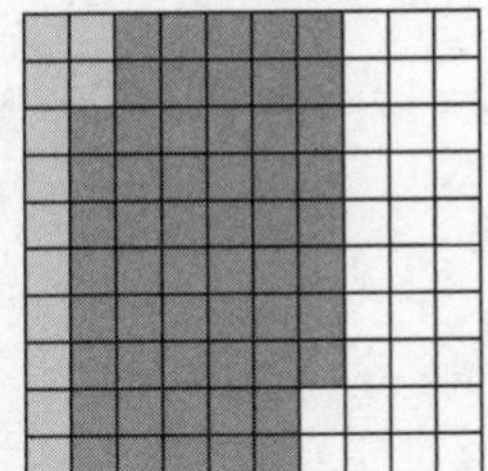

**2.** 0.27 − 0.09 = ________

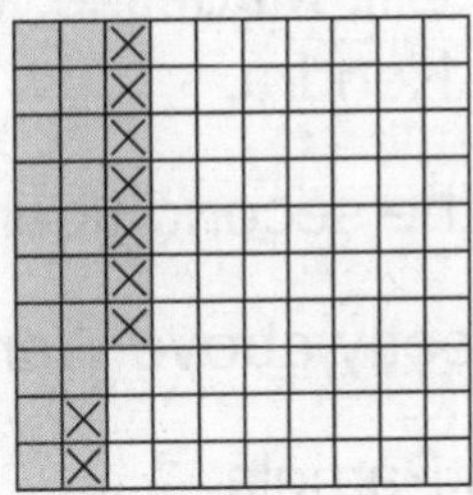

**3.** 0.86 + 0.54 = ________

**4.** 1.27 + 0.75 = ________

**5.** 0.93 − 0.25 = ________

**6.** 1.07 − 0.61 = ________

**7.** 1.13 − 1.02 = ________

**8.** 0.28 + 1.96 = ________

**9.** Is the difference of 1.45 − 0.12 less than or greater than 1? ________

**10.** A bottle of nail polish holds 0.8 ounce. A bottle of perfume holds 0.45 ounce. How many more ounces does a bottle of nail polish hold? ________

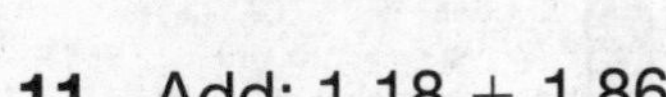

**11.** Add: 1.18 + 1.86

**A** 2.04 **B** 2.94 **C** 3.04 **D** 3.14

**12. Writing to Explain** Explain how to use hundredths grids to subtract 1.65 − 0.98.

______________________

______________________

______________________



 

Name ______________________



# Where Do You Live?

Read the clues to find where each person lives in the apartment building. As you discover where each person lives, write the person's name in the apartment.

1. At Rosebud Terrace, there are 8 apartments. The names of the tenants are Bill, Madeline, Warrick, Pamela, Quincy, Salma, Todd, and Kendra.

   - Salma lives on the second floor.
   - Quincy lives directly above Warrick.
   - Bill lives next to Pamela.
   - Madeline lives to the left of Warrick and to the right of Kendra.
   - Todd lives to the left of Quincy.
   - Pamela lives right above Todd.

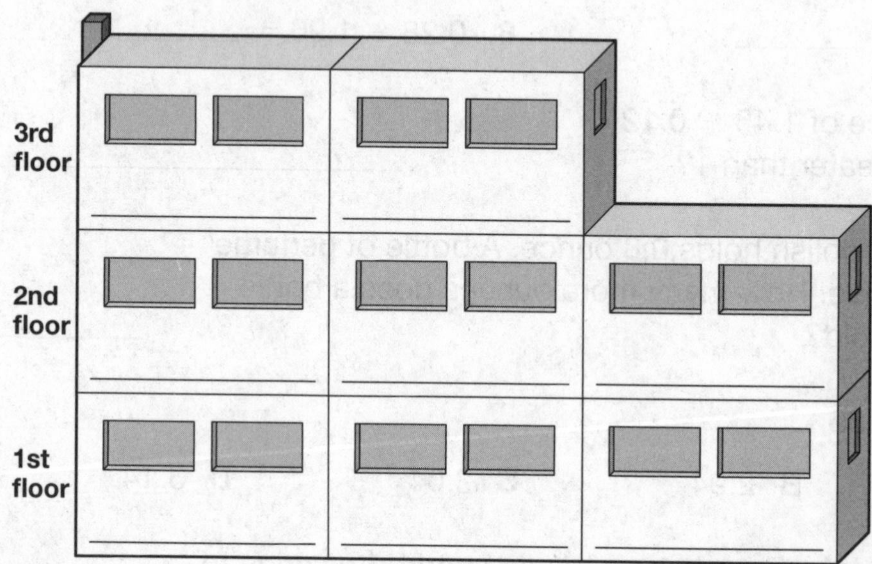


2. Explain how you found each person's place in the apartment building.

______________________________

______________________________

______________________________



 

Name ______________________

Daily Common Core Review
**2-5**

1. A carpenter cuts 3.7 feet from a board that is 10.9 feet long. Which is the best estimate of the length of the remaining board?

   **A** 4 feet
   **B** 7 feet
   **C** 11 feet
   **D** 15 feet

2. The list below shows the things Mark buys at a clothing store.

   Thank You For Shopping at Clark's Clothes Shoppe!

   | Item | Price |
   |---|---|
   | Socks | $ 6.52 |
   | Pants | $ 19.89 |
   | Shirts | $ 21.15 |

   Which is the best estimate of the total Mark spends, not including tax?

   **A** $57
   **B** $48
   **C** $40
   **D** $36

3. James saves $23 each month. How much money has he saved after 7 months?

   ______________________

4. A soccer stadium has 40,218 seats. For one game, 37,842 people come to the stadium. Estimate the number of empty seats at the game to the nearest thousand.

   ______________________

5. Estimate the sum to the nearest whole number.

   29.1 + 78.9 + 41.5

   ______________________

6. Ryan takes 2 pairs of shoes (sneakers and sandals) and 3 pairs of shorts (red, blue, and white) when he goes on a trip. List all the possible outfits with 1 pair of shoes and 1 pair of shorts that Ryan could wear.

   ______________________



 

Name ___________________________________

Reteaching
**2-5**

# Problem Solving: Draw a Picture and Write an Equation

A community center is raising funds to buy a computer. Here is a picture of the sign they put outside the center. How much more money must the center raise?

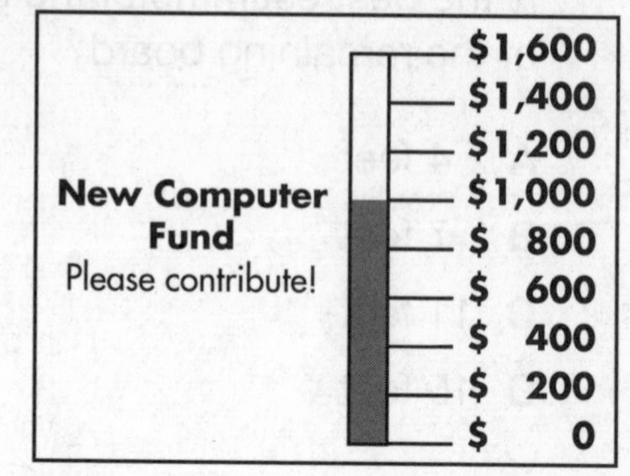


How to write an equation number sentence for a problem:

**One Way**

The goal is $1,600.

So far, $1,000 has been raised.

The amount yet to be raised is the unknown.

Think: The amount raised so far and the amount yet to be raised will reach the goal.

Write an equation.

$$1{,}000 + x = 1{,}600$$

Think: What number added to 1,000 will result in 1,600?

$$1{,}000 + \mathbf{600} = 1{,}600$$

The amount yet to be raised is $600.

**Another Way**

The goal is $1,600.

So far, $1,000 has been raised.

The amount yet to be raised is the unknown.

Think: The difference between the goal and what has been raised so far is the amount yet to be raised.

Write an equation.

$$1{,}600 - 1{,}000 = x$$

Think: What number will result if 1,000 is subtracted from 1,600?

$$1{,}600 - 1{,}000 = \mathbf{600}$$

The amount yet to be raised is $600.

A mason needs 22 bricks to make a stoop. So far he has carried 15 to the site. How many more bricks must he carry?

Draw a picture. Write an equation. Write a number sentence. Solve.

___________________________________



 

Name ______________________________

Practice
**2-5**

# Problem Solving: Draw a Picture and Write an Equation

Write two different equations; then solve each problem.

**1.** Dayana picked apples for 2 hours. She picked 28 apples in the first hour, and at the end of two hours, she had 49. How many apples did she pick during the second hour? ____________

**2.** Dixon bought a pack of pencils and then gave 12 away. He now has 24 left. How many pencils were in the pack of pencils that Dixon bought? ____________

Copy and complete the picture. Then write an equation and solve.

**3.** Rumina is baking 25 muffins for the bake sale. She has already baked 12. How many more does she need to bake?

| 25 muffins in all | |
|---|---|
| 12 | *n* |

______________________________

**4. Estimation** Janet saved 22 dollars one month and 39 dollars the next month. She wants to buy a bicycle that costs $100. About how much more money does she need?

**A** about $40 **B** about $50 **C** about $60 **D** about $70

**5. Writing to Explain** Stefany ran 2 miles each day for 14 days. How many miles did she run in 14 days? Explain two different ways to solve this problem, and then solve.

______________________________

______________________________

Name ______________________

Enrichment
2-5

# Zoo Clues

1. At the zoo, there are 47 armadillos. If 39 of the armadillos are female, how many armadillos are male? Write two different equations, and then solve.

______________________

______________________

2. Carly needs to buy 26 tickets for the monorail ride at the zoo. She bought 17 tickets so far. How many more tickets does Carly need to buy? Write an equation, and then solve.

______________________

______________________

3. There are three species of baboons at the zoo, with a total of 58 baboons in all. If 21 are olive baboons and 35 are sacred baboons, how many are yellow baboons? Write two different equations, and then solve.

______________________

______________________

4. Mark is buying souvenirs at the zoo's gift shop for 35 relatives. He has selected 19 souvenirs so far. How many more souvenirs does Mark need to select? Write an equation, and then solve.

______________________

______________________

5. In Wild Cat Kingdom, the zoo exhibits a total of 77 big cats in all. If 13 are leopards, 18 are tigers, and 29 are lions, how many are jaguars? Write two different equations, and then solve.

______________________

______________________



 

Name ______________________



**1.** The table shows the greatest distance between the Sun and several planets.

**Distances from the Sun**

| Planet | Greatest Distance from the Sun (miles) |
|---|---|
| Mercury | 43,400,000 |
| Jupiter | 507,100,000 |
| Neptune | 2,819,080,000 |

How much farther from the sun is Neptune at its greatest distance than Mercury at its greatest distance?

**A** 463,700,000 miles

**B** 2,775,680,000 miles

**C** 2,862,480,000 miles

**D** 2,862,840,000 miles

**2.** The population of a city is 101,934. The city's suburbs have a population of 29,382. What is the total population of the city and its suburbs?

**A** 120,216

**B** 131,316

**C** 395,754

**D** 405,864

**3.** Yosemite National Park covers 750,000 acres. Mammoth Cave National Park covers 52,830 acres. How many more acres does Yosemite cover than Mammoth Cave?

______________________

**4.** Write a division number sentence using 3, 9, and 27.

______________________

______________________

**5.** Fill in the blank to make the number sentence true.
420,008 − 9,569 =

______________________

**6.** A bank offers savings accounts with these interest rates: 0.809, 0.098, and 0.890. Which rate is the greatest?

______________________



 

Name ______________________

# Adding Decimals

Reteaching
**2-6**

In February, Chantell ran a 5K race in 0.6 hour. She ran another 5K race in May in 0.49 hour. What was her combined time for the two races?

**Step 1:** Write the numbers, lining up the decimal points. Include the zeros to show place value.

$$\begin{array}{r} 0.60 \\ +\ 0.49 \\ \hline \end{array}$$

You can use decimal squares to represent this addition problem.

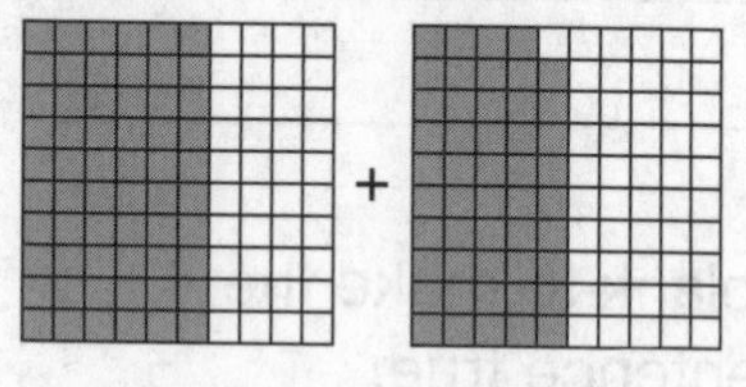

**Step 2:** Add the hundredths.

$$\begin{array}{r} 0.60 \\ +\ 0.49 \\ \hline 9 \end{array}$$

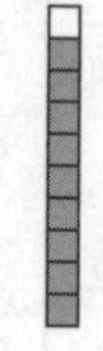

**Step 3:** Add the tenths. Remember to write the decimal point in your answer.

$$\begin{array}{r} \overset{1}{0}.60 \\ +\ 0.49 \\ \hline 1.09 \end{array}$$

Chantell's combined time for the two races was 1.09 hours.

Add.

**1.** 2.97 + 0.35 = ______________

**2.** 13.88 + 7.694 = ______________

**3.** 39.488 + 26.7 = ______________

**4.** 88.8 + 4.277 + 78.95 = ______________

**5.** Is 16.7 a reasonable sum for 7.5 + 9.2? Explain.

______________________________________________

______________________________________________

**6.** How much combined snowfall was there in Milwaukee and Oklahoma City?

______________

| City | Snowfall (inches) in 2000 |
|---|---|
| Milwaukee, WI | 87.8 |
| Baltimore, MD | 27.2 |
| Oklahoma City, OK | 17.3 |



 

Name ______________________

Practice
**2-6**

# Adding Decimals

Add.

**1.** 58.0 + 3.6 

**2.** 40.5 + 22.3 

**3.** 34.587 + 21.098 

**4.** 43.1000 + 8.4388

**5.** 16.036 + 7.009 = __________

**6.** 92.30 + 0.32 = __________

**7.** Reilly adds 45.3 and 3.21. Should his sum be greater than or less than 48? Tell how you know.

______________________

______________________

______________________

In science class, students weighed different amounts of tin. Carmen weighed 4.361 g, Kim weighed 2.704 g, Simon weighed 5.295 g, and Angelica weighed 8.537 g.

**8.** How many grams of tin did Carmen and Angelica have combined?

______________________

**9.** How many grams of tin did Kim and Simon have combined?

______________________

**10.** In December the snowfall was 0.03 in. and in January it was 2.1 in. Which was the total snowfall?

**A** 3.2 in. **B** 2.40 in. **C** 2.13 in. **D** 0.03 in.

**11.** **Writing to Explain** Explain why it is important to line up decimal numbers by their place value when you add or subtract them.

______________________

______________________

______________________



 

Name ________________________________



# Summer Savings

Hazel is earning money this summer by doing chores for her neighbors. She decides to make a bar graph to help her see how much money she makes at each job each week. Show each amount on the graph.

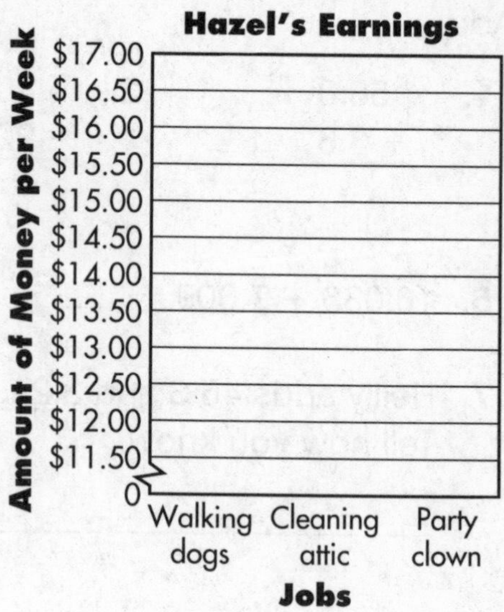


1. Hazel earns $5.50 each time she walks Ms. Duncan's dog, Rose. She walks Rose 3 times each week.

2. Hazel helps Mr. Carson clean his attic two times each week. She earns $6.50 each time.

3. Hazel earns $4.25 per hour when she entertains children as a clown during birthday parties. She works as a clown 4 hours each week.

4. Hazel wants to save money to buy a bicycle for $300.00. If Hazel did all of her jobs each week, how many weeks would she need to work to earn $300.00?

________________________________

5. Hazel is going to volunteer at the humane society. She needs to decide which job she should stop doing to make more time for her volunteer work. Which job do you think Hazel should stop doing? Why?

________________________________

________________________________

________________________________

Name ______________________________

Daily Common Core Review

**2-7**

**1.** Laura keeps track of the amount of gasoline she buys each week.

**Laura's Gasoline Purchases**

| Week | Amount of Gas Bought (gallons) |
|---|---|
| 1 | 12.4 |
| 2 | 10.99 |
| 3 | 11.07 |
| 4 | 9.61 |

How many total gallons of gasoline did Laura buy during Week 1 and Week 2?

**A** 12.23

**B** 22.39

**C** 23.39

**D** 33.40

**2.** Ms. Reyes goes to the garden center. She buys a tree for $40.49 and some soil for $19.90. What is the total amount Ms. Reyes spends?

**A** $42.48

**B** $59.40

**C** $59.59

**D** $60.39

**3.** In a gymnastics meet, the team score is the total of each team member's score.

| Team A | Score | Team B | Score |
|---|---|---|---|
| Gina | 9.052 | Lou | 9.245 |
| Mari | 8.935 | Jen | 9.611 |
| Kim | 8.701 | Pat | 8.003 |
| Ana | 9.008 | Kira | 8.525 |

Which team wins the meet? What is the score of the winning team?

______________________________

**4.** Can you draw a triangle with two obtuse angles?

______________________________

______________________________

______________________________

______________________________

**5.** Mr. Blaine pays Ron, Nan, and Lin $45 to mow and clean up his yard. If Ron, Nan, and Lin share the money equally, how much does each person get?

______________________________



 

Name ____________________



# Subtracting Decimals

Mr. Montoya bought 3.5 lb of ground beef. He used 2.38 lb to make hamburgers. How much ground beef does he have left?

**Step 1:** Write the numbers, lining up the decimal points. Include the zeros to show place value.

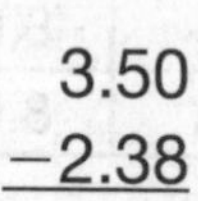

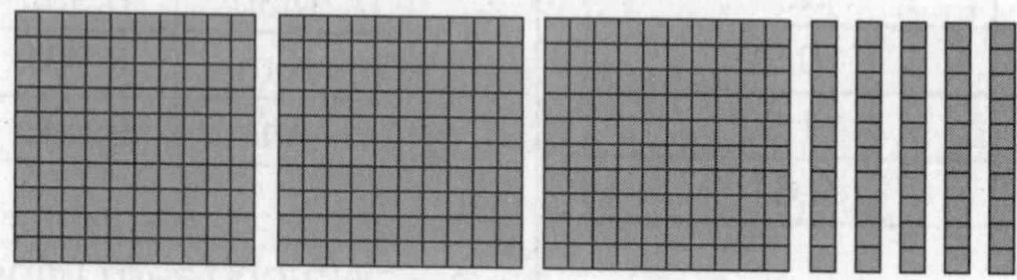

You can use decimal squares to represent this subtraction problem.

**Step 2:** Subtract the hundredths. Regroup if you need to.

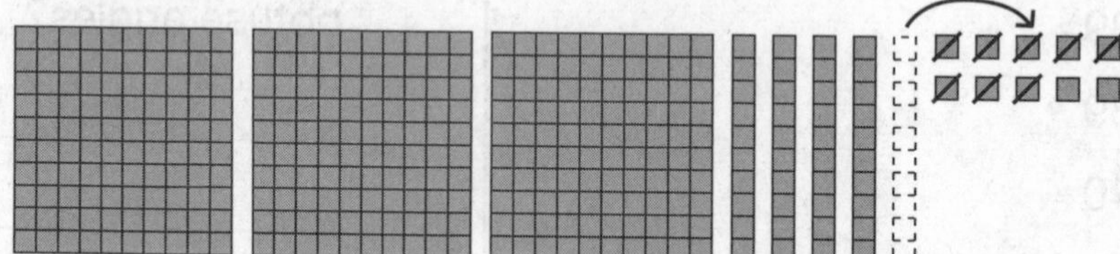

**Step 3:** Subtract the tenths and the ones. Remember to write the decimal point in your answer.

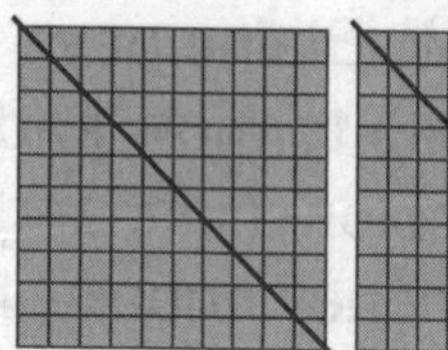

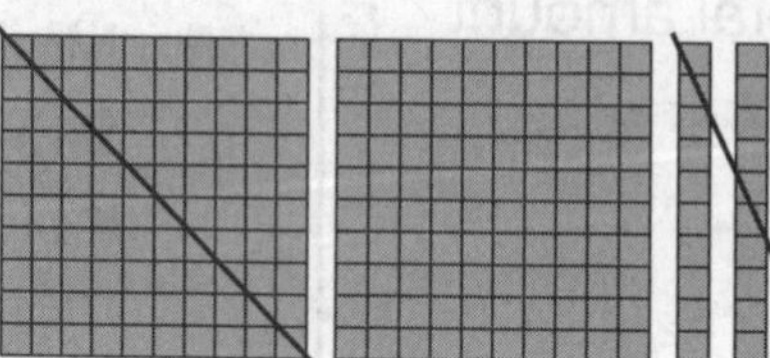

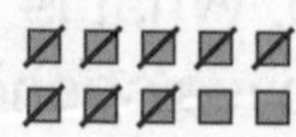

Mr. Montoya has 1.12 lb of ground beef left over.

Subtract.

**1.** 82.7 − 5.59 ____________

**2.** 43.3 − 12.82 ____________

**3.** 7.28 − 4.928 ____________

Name ______________________

Practice
**2-7**

# Subtracting Decimals

Subtract.

**1.** 92.1 − 32.6

**2.** 52.7 − 36.9

**3.** 85.76 − 12.986

**4.** 32.7 − 2.328

**5.** 8.7 − 0.3 = ____________

**6.** 23.3 − 1.32 = ____________

**7.** Kelly subtracted 2.3 from 20 and got 17.7. Explain why this answer is reasonable.

______________________________________________

______________________________________________

At a local swim meet, the second-place swimmer of the 100-m freestyle had a time of 9.33 sec. The first-place swimmer's time was 1.32 sec faster than the second-place swimmer. The third-place time was 13.65 sec.

**8.** What was the time for the first-place swimmer? ____________

**9.** What was the difference in time between the second- and third-place swimmers? ____________

**10.** Miami's annual precipitation in 2000 was 61.05 in. Albany's was 46.92 in. How much greater was Miami's precipitation than Albany's?

**A** 107.97 in. **B** 54.31 in. **C** 14.93 in. **D** 14.13 in.

**11. Writing to Explain** Explain how to subtract 7.6 from 20.39.

______________________________________________

______________________________________________

______________________________________________

______________________________________________

______________________________________________

Name ______________________________

Enrichment **2-7**

# Find Those Numbers!

Fill in the boxes to complete the differences.

**1.**
```
  1 7 . □ 4
−   9 . 3 □
  ---------
    □ . 3 8
```

**2.**
```
   2 . □ □
 − □ . 6 4
 ---------
   1 . 2 9
```

**3.**
```
  1 □ . 4 5
−   7 . 6 □
 ----------
    3 . □ 7
```

**4.**

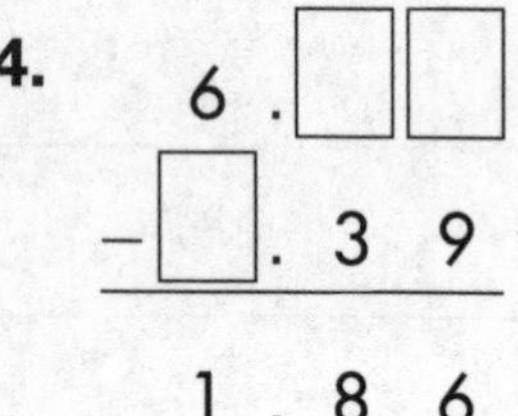


**5.**

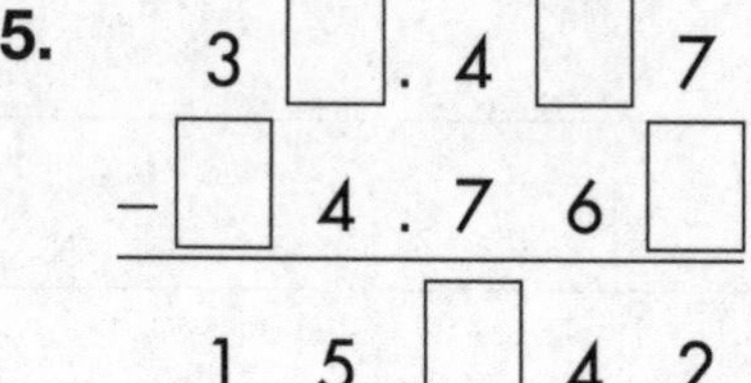


**6.**

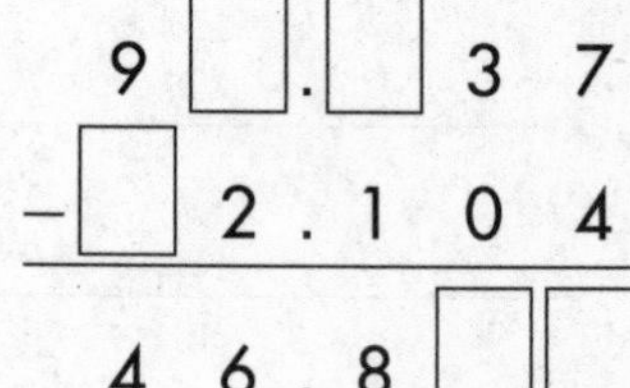


**7.**
```
   □ 2 . □ 3
 − 3 4 . 7 □ □
 -------------
   2 □ . 6 1 8
```

**8.**
```
   □ 4 . 0 □ 8
 − 3 8 . 7 4 □
 -------------
   5 □ . □ 2 6
```

**9.**
```
   □ □ . 7 1 4
 − 3 4 . 8 □
 -------------
   2 9 . □ 0 □
```

Complete the puzzles. Every triangle will be the difference between the rectangle and the oval.

**10.**

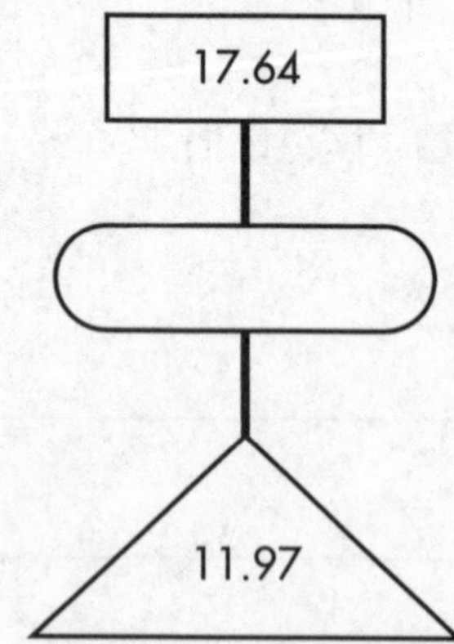


**11.**

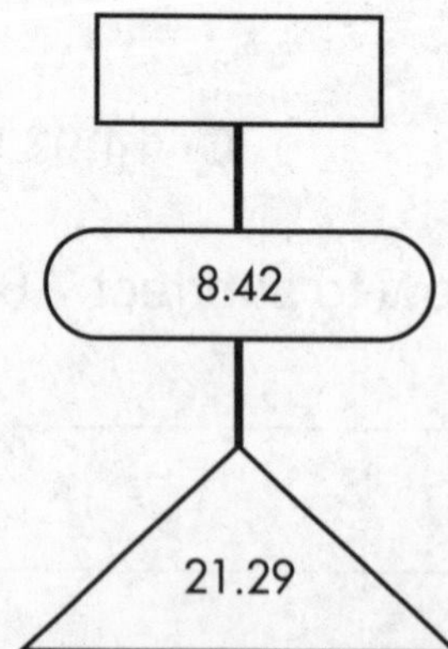


**12.**

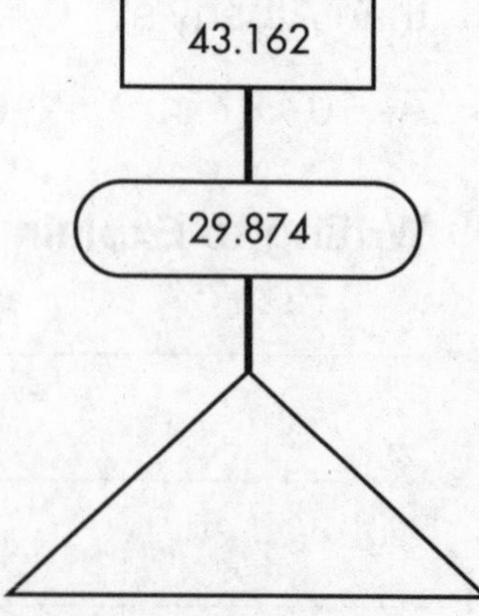

Name ____________________



1. At a ski-jump competition, the first-place jumper has 231.2 points. The last-place jumper has 198.4 points. What is the difference between the scores for first and last place?

   **A** 32.8 points

   **B** 33.2 points

   **C** 41.8 points

   **D** 48.8 points

2. The regular price for a bicycle is $210.19. The sale price is $43.48 less than the regular price. What is the sale price?

   **A** $177.71

   **B** $175.39

   **C** $166.71

   **D** $146.41

3. Which is the best estimate of the weight of a car?

   **A** 2,000 gallons

   **B** 2,000 grams

   **C** 2,000 ounces

   **D** 2,000 pounds

4. Subtract.

   10.06 − 6.101

   ____________________

5. Jana's best time in a swim race so far is 3.058 minutes. What is the slowest she could swim the race and still beat her best time by 0.02 minutes?

   ____________________

6. The table shows the mass of 4 samples.

| | Mass (grams) |
|---|---|
| Sample A | 0.130 |
| Sample B | 0.301 |
| Sample C | 0.031 |
| Sample D | 0.013 |

List the samples in order from least to greatest mass.

____________________

Name ____________________



# Problem Solving: Multiple-Step Problems

Kim has a $10 bill, a $20 bill, and 2 $5 gift certificates. She uses the gift certificates toward the purchase of a CD for $14.00. How much money does Kim have left after buying the CD?

**Read and Understand**

What do you know?

Kim has a ten-dollar bill, a twenty-dollar bill, and two five-dollar gift certificates.

She uses the 2 certificates toward the purchase of a CD that costs $14.00.

What are you trying to find?

How much money does Kim have left after she buys the CD?

**Plan and Solve**

Answer these hidden questions.

How much money does Kim have? $20.00 + $10.00 = $30.00

How much are the two certificates worth? $5.00 + $5.00 = $10.00

How much cash will Kim need to buy the CD? $14.00 − $10.00 = $4.00

Solve the problem.

Money − cash paid for CD = Money left
$30.00 − $4.00 = $26.00

Write the answer in a complete sentence.

Kim has $26 left after buying the CD.

**Look Back and Check**

Is your answer correct?

Yes, $4.00 + $26.00 = $30.00

1. You can also find how much money Kim has left by completing the following expression.

   $10.00 + $20.00 + $5.00 + $5.00 − ____________



 

Name ______________________________

# Problem Solving: Multiple-Step Problems

Solve.

1. Theater tickets for children cost $5. Adult tickets cost $3 more. If 2 adults and 2 children buy theater tickets, what is the total cost?

2. Luis has a $10 bill and three $5 bills. He spends $12.75 on the entrance fee to an amusement park and $8.50 on snacks. How much money does he have left?

3. Alexandra earns $125 from her paper route each month, but she spends about $20 each month on personal expenses. To pay for a school trip that costs $800, about how many months does she need to save money? Explain.

4. Patty is a member of the environmental club. Each weekday, she volunteers for 2 hours. On Saturday and Sunday, she volunteers 3 hours more each day. Which expression shows how to find the number of hours she volunteers in one week?

   **A** 2 + 5

   **B** 2 + 2 + 2 + 2 + 2 + 5 + 5

   **C** 2 + 2 + 2 + 3 + 3

   **D** 2 + 3 + 3

5. Marco's goal is to eat only 2,000 calories each day. One day for breakfast he consumed 310 calories, for lunch he consumed 200 more calories than breakfast, and for dinner he consumed 800. Did he make his goal? Explain.

Name ________________________________

Enrichment

**2-8**

# Ice Cream Parlor Sense

**1.** Gerard has two $5 bills and three $10 bills. He spends $3.85 for a milkshake and $7.98 for a banana split. How much money does he have left?

______________________________

Use the table below for Exercises **2–5**.

| Create Your Own Sundae | Price |
|---|---|
| Basic sundae (one scoop) | $1.99 |
| Extra scoop | $1.25 extra |
| Two extra scoops | $2.50 extra |
| Extras: walnuts, cherries, sprinkles, hot fudge, butterscotch, whipped cream, chocolate shavings | $0.66 apiece |

**2.** Tina wants to make an ice cream sundae with an extra scoop, walnuts, hot fudge, whipped cream, and sprinkles. How much will her ice cream sundae cost?

______________________________

**3.** Tina found a coupon in her wallet for $1.50 off any ice cream sundae. She used it for her order in Problem 2 and added cherries to her sundae. How much will her ice cream sundae cost now?

______________________________

**4.** Jamaal has four $5 bills and two $10 bills. He makes an ice cream sundae with two extra scoops, hot fudge, whipped cream, and chocolate shavings. After he pays, how much money does he have left?

______________________________

**5.** If Jamaal buys an ice cream sundae identical to the one in Problem 4 for Tyler, how much money does he have left now?

______________________________

Name ______________________

Daily Common Core Review
**3-1**

**1.** Jennie has 2 cats, both of which just had kittens. Zippy has twice as many kittens as Fuzzy. Jennie's friends adopt 5 of the kittens. What do you need to know to find out how many of the kittens Jennie keeps?

**A** The total number of kittens

**B** How old the kittens are now

**C** How many friends Jennie has

**D** The date when the kittens were born

**2.** Pedro's weekly salary is $372.29. He has $45.50 taken out of his salary to pay for insurance and savings. How much is left for Pedro's paycheck?

**A** $226.69

**B** $326.79

**C** $333.39

**D** $367.74

**3.** An animal rescue center has 51 reptiles, 34 birds, and 16 mammals. Which is the best estimate of the total number of animals?

**A** 120

**B** 100

**C** 70

**D** 50

**4.** A marathon is a running race that is about 26.219 miles long. What is the value of the 9 in this distance?

______________________

**5.** Name the shape below.

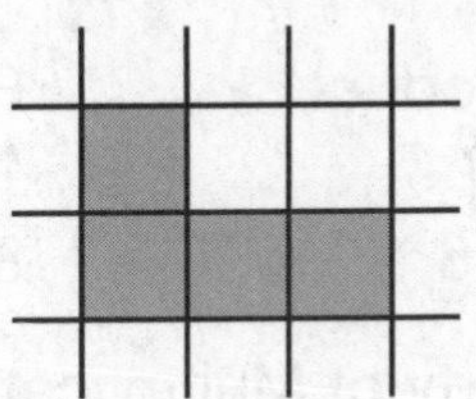

______________________

**6.** Write *five and four hundred three thousandths* in standard form.

______________________

Name ____________________

Reteaching **3-1**

# Multiplication Properties

You can use multiplication properties to help you multiply more easily.

Associative Property of Multiplication
You can change the grouping of the factors. The product stays the same.

$(3 \times 4) \times 4 = 48$ ↓ Factors, Product ↑ $12 \times 4 = 48$

$3 \times (4 \times 4) = 48$ ↓ Factors, Product ↑ $3 \times 16 = 48$

Commutative Property of Multiplication
You can change the order of the factors. The product stays the same.

$7 \times 4 = 28$ ↓ Factors, Product

$4 \times 7 = 28$ ↓ Factors, Product

Zero Property of Multiplication
When one of the factors is 0, the product is always 0.

$3 \times 0 = 0$ ↓ Factors, Product

$0 \times 3 = 0$ ↓ Factors, Product

Identity Property of Multiplication
When one of the factors is 1, the product is always the other factor.

Identify the multiplication property or properties used in each equation.

**1.** $100 \times 0 = 0$ ____________

**2.** $7 \times 2 = 2 \times 7$ ____________

**3.** $1 \times 55 = 55$ ____________

**4.** $(6 \times 7) \times 9 = 6 \times (7 \times 9)$ ____________

Use the multiplication properties to determine what number must be in the box.

**5.** $5 \times 4 = \square \times 5$

**6.** $99 \times \square = 99$

**7.** $(3 \times 12) \times \square = 3 \times (12 \times 8)$

**8.** $\square \times 1 = 0$

**9.** $\square \times 2 = 2 \times 50$

**10.** $(16 \times \square) \times 25 = 16 \times (33 \times 25)$



 

Name ______________________



# Multiplication Properties

In **1** through **5**, write the multiplication property used in each equation.

**1.** $53 \times 6 = 6 \times 53$ ______________________

**2.** $0 \times 374{,}387 = 0$ ______________________

**3.** $5 \times (11 \times 4) = (5 \times 11) \times 4$ ______________________

**4.** $42 \times 1 = 42$ ______________________

**5.** $14 \times 5 = 5 \times 14$ ______________________

**6.** Chan bought 2 large frozen yogurts at $1.50 each and 1 small bottle of water for $1.00. How much did she pay in total?

______________________

**7.** Dan has 4 shelves. He has exactly 10 books on each shelf. Judy has 10 shelves. She has exactly 4 books on each shelf. Who has more books? Explain.

______________________

______________________

**8.** If $3 \times 8 \times 12 = 8 \times 3 \times n$, what is the value of $n$?

**A** 3 **B** 8 **C** 12 **D** 18

**9.** Write a definition for the Associative Property of Multiplication in your own words and explain how you would use it to compute $4 \times 25 \times 27$ mentally.

______________________

______________________

______________________

______________________



 

Name ____________________

Enrichment
**3-1**

# Which Property?

For questions **1–4,** write the multiplication property that makes the statement true.

**1.** $7 \times 49 = 49 \times 7$

____________________

**2.** $891 \times 0 = 0$

____________________

**3.** $1 \times 246 = 246$

____________________

**4.** $6 \times (38 \times 19) = (6 \times 38) \times 19$

____________________

**5.** How can knowing the multiplication properties help you evaluate $5 \times (20 \times 63)$?

____________________

____________________

**6.** If you multiply any number by 1, can the product ever be greater than that number? Explain.

____________________

____________________

Use the multiplication properties to determine what number must be in the box.

**7.** $2{,}378 \times 5 \times \square = 0$

**8.** $3 \times (9 \times 17) = (3 \times 9) \times \square$

**9.** $657 \times \square = 657$

**10.** $264 \times \square = 39 \times 264$



 

Name ______________________________

Daily Common Core Review
**3-2**

**1.** Roberto and Adam have the same number of pennies. Roberto put his pennies in 2 stacks of 6 pennies each. Adam puts his pennies in 6 stacks. How many pennies are in each of Adam's stacks?

**A** 2

**B** 4

**C** 8

**D** 12

**2.** The table shows the scores for four divers in a diving meet.

**Diving Meet Scores**

| Diver | Score |
|---|---|
| Jamal | 25.050 |
| Kelly | 20.505 |
| Luis | 25.005 |
| Marco | 20.055 |

Which diver is in third place?

**A** Jamal

**B** Kelly

**C** Luis

**D** Marco

**3.** Kim's farm is 1,292 acres. Jack's farm is 1,104 acres. Which is the best estimate of the difference in size between Kim's farm and Jack's farm?

**A** 400 acres

**B** 200 acres

**C** 100 acres

**D** 90 acres

**4.** Fill in each box to make an example of the given property.

| Identity Property of *Addition* | Identity Property of *Multiplication* |
|---|---|
| 25 + ☐ = 25 | 25 × ☐ = 25 |

**5.** A football stadium has 81,296 seats. Then the stadium's owner adds 10,795 seats. What is the new total number of seats?

______________________

**6.** A copy machine can make 36 copies in 1 minute. How many copies can the machine make in 10 minutes?

______________________



 

Name ______________________



# Using Mental Math to Multiply

You can also use patterns to multiply mentally.

Fact: 6 × 8 = **48**

| | |
|---|---|
| 60 × 8 = **48**0 | 6 × 80 = **48**0 |
| 600 × 8 = **4,8**00 | 60 × 80 = **4,8**00 |
| 6,000 × 8 = **48,**000 | 600 × 80 = **48,**000 |
| 60,000 × 8 = **48**0,000 | 6,000 × 80 = **48**0,000 |

Pattern: Notice that the product is always the digits 48 followed by the total number of zeros that are in the factors.

Find 30 × 3 × 50.

Use the Commutative and Associative Properties of Multiplication to regroup.

(30 × 50) × 3

1,500 × 3 = 4,500

| Commutative Property of Multiplication | Associative Property of Multiplication |
|---|---|
| You can multiply factors in any order.<br>15 × 9 = 9 × 15 | You can change the grouping of factors.<br>(8 × 20) × 5 = 8 × (20 × 5) |

Find each product. Use patterns and properties to compute mentally.

**1.** 80 × 90 = ______________ **2.** 40 × 800 = ______________

**3.** 5 × 10 × 20 = ______________ **4.** 4 × 30 × 25 = ______________

**5.** You know that 6 × 7 = 42. How can you find 60 × 700?

______________________________________________

______________________________________________

______________________________________________



 

Name ____________________

Practice
**3-2**

# Using Mental Math to Multiply

Use mental math to find each product.

**1.** $150 \times 20 =$ ______

**2.** $0 \times 50 \times 800 =$ ______

**3.** $500 \times 40 =$ ______

**4.** $120 \times 50 =$ ______

**5.** $60 \times 70 \times 1 =$ ______

**6.** $9{,}000 \times 80 =$ ______

**7.** $100 \times 10 \times 1 =$ ______

**8.** $1{,}800 \times 20 \times 0 =$ ______

**9.** $30 \times 20 =$ ______

**10.** $1{,}400 \times 2{,}000 =$ ______

**11.** $7{,}000 \times 50 \times 1 =$ ______

**12.** $1{,}000 \times 200 \times 30 =$ ______

**13.** A googol is a large number that is the digit one followed by one hundred zeros. If you multiply a googol by 100, how many zeros will that product have?

______

**14.** Gregorios drives 200 miles per day for 10 days. How many miles did he drive in all?

______

**15.** If $a \times b \times c = 0$, and $a$ and $b$ are integers greater than 10, what must $c$ equal?

**A** 0 **B** 1 **C** 2 **D** 10

**16.** SungHee empties her piggy bank and finds that she has 200 quarters, 150 dimes, and 300 pennies. How much money does she have? Explain.

______

______



 

Name ____________________

Enrichment
**3-2**

# Find the Products

1. Kaitlyn and Brian are ordering stickers. A carton of stickers has 20 packets with 600 stickers in each packet. If Kaitlyn and Brian ordered 20 cartons, how many stickers did they order? Show your work.

2. Jason needs to explain to his class how to use mental math to find the product of $400{,}000 \times 50{,}000$. What should Jason tell his class?

3. Amy practices yoga 20 minutes each day before school and 30 minutes each day after school. She attends school Monday through Friday. How many minutes does Amy practice yoga in 4 weeks? Show your work.

4. Mr. Shea is collecting pennies from gumball machines in arcades. Each arcade has 10 gumball machines with 500 pennies in each machine. If Mr. Shea visits 30 arcades, how many pennies will he collect? Show your work.

5. Brad volunteers at the nursing home each Saturday for 40 minutes and each Sunday for 30 minutes. He takes two weeks off for vacation each year. How many minutes does Brad volunteer in one year? Show your work.

Name ______________________________

Daily Common Core Review
**3-3**

1. Mr. Johnson works 80 hours each pay period. His salary is $20 per hour. How much money does he earn in 10 pay periods?

   **A** $160,000

   **B** $16,000

   **C** $1,600

   **D** $160

2. Marti, Joel, Oscar, Lucas, and Quentin each ate 2,000 calories per day for 6 days. What is the total number of calories they ate?

   **A** 10,000

   **B** 12,000

   **C** 30,000

   **D** 60,000

3. Emily buys a CD for $12.07, including tax. She gives the clerk a $20 bill. How much change should she receive?

   **A** $8.93

   **B** $8.07

   **C** $7.93

   **D** $7.07

4. Each day, a car goes through the intersection of Main Street and Oak Road 300 times. How many times does a car go through this intersection in 300 days?

   ______________________________

5. Write a number sentence to show the Associative Property of Addition.

   ______________________________

   ______________________________

   ______________________________

6. A restaurant serves 42 chicken dinners and 18 steak dinners. Let *m* be the difference between the numbers of chicken and steak dinners.

   **a.** Draw a picture you could use to find *m*.

   **b.** What is the value of *m*?

   ______________________________



 

Name ______________________



# Estimating Products

A bus service drives passengers between Milwaukee and Chicago every day. They travel from city to city a total of 8 times each day. The distance between the two cities is 89 mi. In the month of February, there are 28 days. The company's budget allows for 28,000 total miles for February. Is 28,000 mi a reasonable budget mileage amount?

**One Way to Estimate**

Estimate 28 × 8 × 89.

Use rounding.

You can round 89 to 100 and 8 to 10. Then multiply.

28 × 10 × 100 = 280 × 100 = 28,000

Because this is an overestimate, there are enough miles.

**Another Way to Estimate**

Estimate 28 × 8 × 89.

Use compatible numbers.

Replace 28 with 30, 89 with 90, and 8 with 10. 30, 90, and 10 are compatible numbers because they are close to the actual numbers in the problem and they are easier to multiply. Now the problem becomes 30 × 90 × 10.

| | |
|---|---|
| 30 × 90 = 2,700 | Multiply 3 × 9, then place two zeros after the product. |
| 2,700 × 10 = 27,000 | Multiply 27 × 1 using the Identity Property of Multiplication, then place three zeros after the product. |

In the estimate, we used numbers greater than the original numbers, so the answer is an overestimate.

28,000 total miles is a reasonable budget amount.

Estimate each product. Use rounding or compatible numbers.

**1.** 42 × 5 × 90 = ______________

**2.** 27 × 98 × 4 = ______________

Mrs. Carter ordered new supplies for Memorial Hospital.

**3.** About how much will it cost to purchase 48 electronic thermometers?

______________________

**4.** About how much will it cost to purchase 96 pillows?

______________________

**Supplies**

| Item | Price |
|---|---|
| Electronic thermometers | $19 each |
| Pulse monitors | $189 each |
| Pillows | $17 each |
| Telephones | $19 each |

Name ______________________

Practice

**3-3**

# Estimating Products

Estimate each product.

**1.** 68 × 21 = ______ **2.** 5 × 101 = ______ **3.** 151 × 21 = ______

**4.** 99 × 99 = ______ **5.** 87 × 403 = ______ **6.** 19 × 718 = ______

**7.** 39 × 51 = ______ **8.** 47 × 29 × 11 = ______ **9.** 70 × 27 = ______

**10.** 69 × 21 × 23 = ______ **11.** 7 × 616 = ______ **12.** 8,880 × 30 = ______

**13.** Give three numbers whose product is about 9,000.

______

**Electronics Prices**

| | |
|---|---|
| CD player | $ 74.00 |
| MP3 player | $ 99.00 |
| CD/MP3 player | $199.00 |
| AM/FM radio | $ 29.00 |

**14.** About how much would it cost to buy 4 CD/MP3 players and 3 MP3 players?

______

**15.** Which is the closest estimate for the product of 2 × 19 × 5?

**A** 1,150 **B** 200 **C** 125 **D** 50

**16.** Explain how you know whether an estimate of a product is an overestimate or an underestimate.

______

______

______

______



 

Name ______________________________



# Dog Wash

Toni and four of her friends are organizing a dog wash to raise money for service dogs for people with disabilities. They will be able to use the equipment at the local dog grooming shop, but they must purchase shampoo and towels. The group expects to wash 60 dogs. They plan to use 18 towels.

1. Complete both charts by writing the estimated total cost for each package or container.

| Towels | Cost per Pack | Estimated Total Cost |
|---|---|---|
| **A.** Pack of 3 | $4.12 | |
| **B.** Pack of 6 | $6.89 | |
| **C.** Pack of 9 | $8.95 | |

| Shampoo | Cost per Container | Estimated Total Cost |
|---|---|---|
| **1.** For 5 dogs | $0.97 | |
| **2.** For 10 dogs | $1.53 | |
| **3.** For 15 dogs | $3.08 | |

2. Toni believes if they purchase the least expensive shampoo, they will have to use three times the amount to get the dogs clean. Write a new estimate for the cost of the least expensive shampoo.

______________________________

3. The least expensive towels are not as absorbent as the others. Toni expects that they will need twice the number of towels to dry the dogs. Write a new estimate for the cost of the least expensive towels.

______________________________

4. Which packs of towels and containers of shampoo should Toni and her friends choose? Why?

______________________________

______________________________

______________________________


 

Name ______________________________



**1.** Dr. Perez has been a doctor for 24 years. He sees each patient for 1 hour. Dr. Perez worked 30 days last month and saw 7 patients each day.

Which piece of information is **NOT** needed to find the total time Dr. Perez spent with patients last month?

**A** The total time he spends with each patient
**B** The total number of patients he saw each day
**C** The total time he has been working as a doctor
**D** The total number of days he worked last month

**2.** What is the difference between 403,951 and 135,211?

**A** 200,000
**B** 221,365
**C** 539,162
**D** 268,740

**3.** A worker paints a 5.2-foot wide crosswalk on a street. Her boss tells her to make the crosswalk 1.25 feet wider. How wide is the finished crosswalk?

**A** 1.25 feet
**B** 1.77 feet
**C** 6.27 feet
**D** 6.45 feet

**4.** Gina takes a group of her friends out for lunch. She buys a bottle of water, a sandwich, and a salad for herself and each friend. The water costs $1.19 for each bottle. One sandwich costs $2.35. Each salad is $1.99.

Can you find the total amount of money Gina spends?

______________________________

______________________________

______________________________

______________________________

**5.** The state of Texas has 261,197 square miles of land and 6,784 square miles of water. How many more square miles of land does Texas have than water?

______________________________

______________________________

**6.** What is the perimeter of this rectangle?

24 cm
100 cm

______________________________



 

Name ____________________



# Exponents

You can use exponential notation to write a number that is being multiplied by itself.

There are two parts in exponential notation. The **base** tells you what factor is being multiplied. The **exponent** tells you how many of that factor should be multiplied together. The exponent is *not* a factor.

exponent
↓
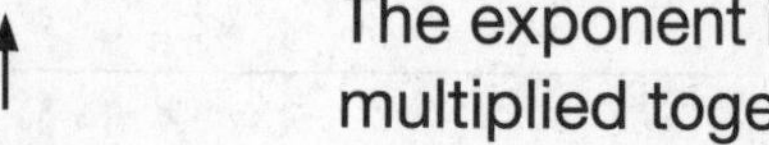

$8^2 = 8 \times 8$ The base is 8, so 8 is the factor to be multiplied. The exponent is 2, so 2 factors of 8 should be multiplied together.
↑
base

You can write $8^2$ in two other forms.

In **expanded** form, you write out your factors. Since $8^2$ means you multiply two factors of 8, $8^2$ in expanded form is $8 \times 8$.

In **standard** form, you write down the product of the factors. Since $8 \times 8 = 64$, 64 is the standard form of $8^2$.

Write in exponential notation.

**1.** $2 \times 2 \times 2$ ____________

**2.** $6 \times 6 \times 6 \times 6 \times 6$ ____________

Write in expanded form.

**3.** $1^4$ ____________

**4.** $5^3$ ____________

Write in standard form.

**5.** $2 \times 2 \times 2 \times 2$ ____________

**6.** $8^3$ ____________

**7.** A used car lot has 9 lanes for cars and 9 rows for cars in each lane. What is the exponential notation for the number of spaces on the lot? Can the owner fit 79 cars on the lot?

____________________

Name ______________________



# Exponents

For questions **1–4**, write in exponential notation.

**1.** $13 \times 13 \times 13$ ______________

**2.** $8 \times 8 \times 8 \times 8 \times 8 \times 8$ ______________

**3.** $64 \times 64$ ______________

**4.** $4 \times 4 \times 4 \times 4$
$\times 4 \times 4 \times 4 \times 4$ ______________

For questions **5–8**, write in expanded form.

**5.** $2^5$ ______________

**6.** 20 squared ______________

**7.** $11^4$ ______________

**8.** 9 cubed ______________

For questions **9–12**, write in standard form.

**9.** $4 \times 4 \times 4$ ______________

**10.** 14 squared ______________

**11.** $6^5$ ______________

**12.** $9 \times 9 \times 9 \times 9$ ______________

**13.** Which of these numbers, written in expanded form, is equal to 625?

**A** $5 \times 5 \times 5 \times 5$
**B** $5 \times 5$
**C** $5 \times 5 \times 5$
**D** $5 \times 5 \times 5 \times 5 \times 5$

**14.** Find the number equal to 6 raised to the second power.

**A** 18
**B** 36
**C** 6
**D** 12

**15.** Explain what 4 raised to the fourth power means.

______________________________________________

______________________________________________



 

Name ______________________

Enrichment

3-4

# Writing Large Numbers

Write the following numbers in exponential notation.

**1.** 1,000,000 __________

**2.** $99 \times 99 \times 99 \times 99$ __________

**3.** 49 __________

**4.** 16 __________

Write the following numbers in standard form.

**5.** 8 cubed __________

**6.** 19 squared __________

**7.** $7^4$ __________

**8.** $10^9$ __________

Write the following numbers in expanded form.

**9.** $97^6$ __________

**10.** 481 squared __________

**11.** $375^5$ __________

**12.** 52 cubed __________

**13.** Find the number that equals 121 when it is squared. ________

**14.** Find the number that equals 216 when it is cubed. ________

**15.** Barbara has a packing carton that is 14 inches long, 14 inches wide, and 14 inches tall. If the volume of the carton is the length times the width times the height, show the number of cubic inches the carton holds in exponential notation, expanded form, and standard form.

______________________________

**16.** Bret's uncle owns a square of land that is 10 miles long on each side. Is that the same as 10 $mi^2$?

______________________________

______________________________



 

Name ____________________

Daily Common Core Review

**3-5**

**1.** Which answer shows the algebraic expression for the following phrase?

Five times a number plus three

**A** $5n + 3$
**B** $5 + 3n$
**C** $5 \times 3 + n$
**D** $5 + n \times 3$

**2.** Evaluate the following expression.

$(32 + 12) - 17$

**A** 37
**B** 33
**C** 28
**D** 27

**3.** Evaluate the following expression for $y = 11$.

$63 - 4y$

**A** 18
**B** 19
**C** 21
**D** 29

**4.** To complete a project, Roshan must spend 3 hours on research and 2 hours writing each page. Write an expression for the total hours she needs.

____________________

Use the expression to evaluate for 12 pages.

____________________

Use the expression to evaluate for 21 pages.

____________________

**5.** Evaluate the following expressions for $x = 33$.

$288 - 4x$

____________________

$10x + 17$

____________________

$8x - 201$

____________________

Name ______________________________________



# Distributive Property

Hector's rock collection is in 7 cases. Each case holds 28 rocks. How many rocks are in Hector's collection? You can use the Distributive Property to find the product of $7 \times 28$.

**Step 1.** Split 28 into $20 + 8$.
$7 \times 28 = 7 \times (20 + 8)$

**Step 2.** Multiply 7 times each part of the sum.
$(7 \times 20) + (7 \times 8)$

$140 + 56$

**Step 3.** Use addition to find the sum.
$140 + 56 = 196$

OR

**Step 1.** Split 28 into $30 - 2$.
$7 \times 28 = 7 \times (30 - 2)$

**Step 2.** Multiply 7 times each part of the difference.
$(7 \times 30) - (7 \times 2)$

$210 - 14$

**Step 3.** Use subtraction to find the difference.
$210 - 14 = 196$

So, $7 \times 28 = 196$. Hector has 196 rocks in his collection.

---

Rewrite using the Distributive Property. Then find the product.

**1.** $3 \times 42$ ______ **2.** $39 \times 5$ ______ **3.** $6 \times 147$ ______ **4.** $19 \times 70$ ______

**5.** $54 \times 67$ ______ **6.** $90 \times 83$ ______ **7.** $364 \times 26$ ______ **8.** $45 \times 678$ ______

For questions **9** through **12**, find the value of *n*.

**9.** $4 \times 62 = (4 \times n) + (4 \times 2)$ ______

**10.** $79 \times 20 = (80 \times 20) - (n \times 20)$ ______

**11.** $53 \times 118 = (53 \times 100) + (n \times 18)$ ______

**12.** $352 \times 75 = (n \times 75) + (50 \times 75) + (2 \times 75)$ ______

**13.** Joey's class is collecting food for the school canned food drive. There are 28 children in Joey's class. Each child brought in 15 cans of food. Use the Distributive Property to find out how many cans of food Joey's class collected.

______________________________________



 

Name ______________________________

Practice **3-5**

# Distributive Property

Use the Distributive Property to multiply mentally.

**1.** $5 \times 607 =$ __________ **2.** $16 \times 102 =$ __________

**3.** $7 \times 420 =$ __________ **4.** $265 \times 5 =$ __________

**5.** $44 \times 60 =$ __________ **6.** $220 \times 19 =$ __________

**7.** $45 \times 280 =$ __________ **8.** $341 \times 32 =$ __________

**9.** Fill in the blanks to show how the Distributive Property can be used to find $10 \times 147$.

$10 \times (150 - 3) = (10 \times 150) - ($__________ $\times 3) =$

$1{,}500 -$ __________ $=$ __________

**10.** In 1990, there were 1,133 tornadoes in the U.S. If there were the same number of tornadoes for 10 years in a row, what would be the 10-year total?

______________________________

**11.** There were 1,071 tornadoes in the U.S. in 2000. What is the number of tornadoes multiplied by 20?

______________________________

**12.** If $4 \times 312 = 4 \times 300 + n$, which is the value of $n$?

**A** 4 **B** 12 **C** 48 **D** 300

**13.** Margaret said that she used the Distributive Property to solve $4 \times 444$. Is her answer shown below correct? Explain.

$4 \times 444 = 4 \times (400 + 40 + 4) =$

$(4 \times 400) + (4 \times 40) + (4 \times 4) =$

$1{,}600 + 160 + 16 = 1{,}776$

______________________________

______________________________

Name ____________________



# Find the Products

**1.** Circle the letter of the problem that has the greatest product.

**A** $85 \times 41$ **B** $224 \times 13$ **C** $471 \times 5$

**2.** Write an estimate for each product in Exercise 1.

**A** ______ **B** ______ **C** ______

**3.** Find the exact product for each problem in Exercise 1.

**A** ______ **B** ______ **C** ______

**4.** Circle the letter of the problem that has a product that is about four times greater than the product of one of the other problems.

**A** $201 \times 79$ **B** $509 \times 11$ **C** $198 \times 20$

**5.** Write an estimate for each product in Exercise 4.

**A** ______ **B** ______ **C** ______

**6.** Find the exact product for each problem in Exercise 4.

**A** ______ **B** ______ **C** ______

**7.** **Writing to Explain** What are some real-life situations in which you would not want an estimate that is too low or too high? Write one example of each.

______________________________

______________________________

______________________________

______________________________

______________________________



 

Name ______________________________

Daily Common Core Review
**3-6**

**1.** Ms. Sakura teaches her 27 students to make folded-paper birds. Each student can make about 2 birds in 1 minute. About how many birds can all the students make in 55 minutes?

**A** 3,000
**B** 1,500
**C** 100
**D** 60

**2.** Yesterday, the snow at the peak of Bleak Mountain was 450.23 inches deep. Last night, a snowstorm added another 14.095 inches of snow. Now, how deep is the snow at the peak of Bleak Mountain?

**A** 436.135 inches
**B** 464.325 inches
**C** 465.18 inches
**D** 591.18 inches

**3.** What digit could be in the ten millions place of a number that is less than 55,000,000 but greater than 25,000,000?

______________________________

**4.** Four athletes are keeping track of how much they walk each day during the summer. The table shows how many kilometers each athlete walked on Saturday.

| **Athlete** | **Distance Walked (km)** |
|---|---|
| Anne | 16.3 |
| Keisha | 16.48 |
| Michael | 16.5 |
| Terrell | 15.69 |

Who walked the farthest?

______________________________

**5.** Pecan trees grow about 19 inches per year. Fill in the blanks below to <u>estimate</u> how many inches of growth a group of 882 pecan trees would gain in 5 years. Is your answer an **overestimate** or an **underestimate**?

______ × ______ × ______ = ______

______________________________

**6.** A company earned $4,311,608,242 last year. This year, the company earned $5,097,745,368. How much more money did the company earn this year?

______________________________



 

Name ____________________



# Multiplying by 1-Digit Numbers

Mr. McGuire drives his truck 275 miles each day. How far does he drive in 3 days?

Find 275 × 3.

| | | |
|---|---|---|
| **Step 1:** Multiply the ones. Regroup if necessary. | **What You Think** 3 × 5 ones = 15 ones Regroup 15 ones as 1 ten and 5 ones. | **What You Write** |

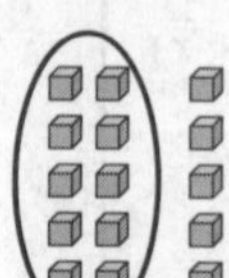

$$\begin{array}{r} {}^{1}\\ 275 \\ \times\ 3 \\ \hline 5 \end{array}$$

| | | |
|---|---|---|
| **Step 2:** Multiply the tens. Regroup if necessary. | **What You Think** 3 × 7 tens = 21 tens 21 tens + 1 ten = 22 tens Regroup as 2 hundreds and 2 tens. | **What You Write** |

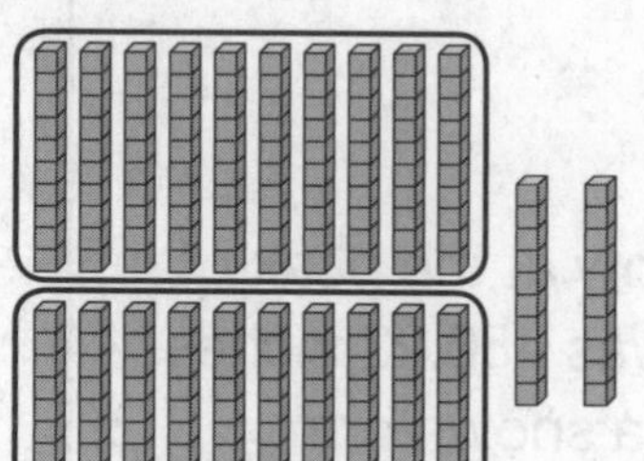

$$\begin{array}{r} {}^{2\,1}\\ 275 \\ \times\ 3 \\ \hline 25 \end{array}$$

| | | |
|---|---|---|
| **Step 3:** Multiply the hundreds. Regroup if necessary. | **What You Think** 3 × 2 hundreds = 6 hundreds 6 hundreds + 2 hundreds = 8 hundreds No need to regroup. | **What You Write** |

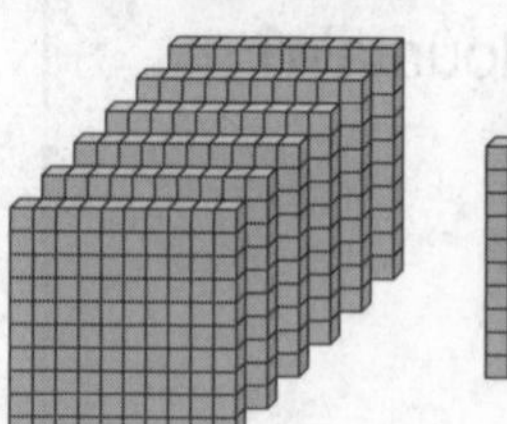

$$\begin{array}{r} {}^{2\,1}\\ 275 \\ \times\ 3 \\ \hline 825 \end{array}$$

Mr. McGuire drives 825 miles in 3 days.

Find each product. Estimate to check that your answer is reasonable.

**1.** 31 × 7 ________ **2.** 29 × 4 ________ **3.** 88 × 6 ________

**4.** 25 × 9 ________ **5.** 102 × 8 ________ **6.** 211 × 7 ________

**7.** 552 × 3 ________ **8.** 471 × 9 ________ **9.** 73 × 4 ________

**10.** 266 × 8 ________ **11.** 390 × 2 ________ **12.** 514 × 6 ________

**13. Estimation** Estimate the product of 48 and 7. Do you have an underestimate or overestimate?

_______________________________________

_______________________________________

Name ____________________

Practice
**3-6**

# Multiplying by 1-Digit Numbers

Find each product. Estimate to check that your answer is reasonable.

**1.** $58 \times 3 =$ __________ **2.** $49 \times 8 =$ __________

**3.** $83 \times 5 =$ __________ **4.** $95 \times 6 =$ __________

**5.** $273 \times 4 =$ __________ **6.** $35 \times 8 =$ __________

**7.** $789 \times 6 =$ __________ **8.** $643 \times 7 =$ __________

**9.** $\begin{array}{r} 68 \\ \times\ 2 \\ \hline \end{array}$ **10.** $\begin{array}{r} 582 \\ \times\ 5 \\ \hline \end{array}$ **11.** $\begin{array}{r} 84 \\ \times\ 4 \\ \hline \end{array}$ **12.** $\begin{array}{r} 926 \\ \times\ 7 \\ \hline \end{array}$

**13.** Xavier painted five portraits and wants to sell them for 36 dollars each. How much money will he make if he sells all five? __________

**14.** A farmer wants to build a square pigpen. The length of one side of the pen is 13 ft. How many feet of fencing should the farmer buy? __________

**15.** Jasmine wants to buy 4 green bags for 18 dollars each and 3 purple bags for 15 dollars each. She has 100 dollars. How much more money does she need? __________

**16.** A regular octagon is a figure that has eight sides with equal lengths. If one side of a regular octagon is 14 inches long, what is the perimeter of the entire octagon?

**A** 148 in. **B** 140 in. **C** 112 in. **D** 84 in.

**17.** Why is 2,482 not a reasonable answer for $542 \times 6$?

______________________________

______________________________

______________________________

Name ______________________



# Cross-Country Trip

Mr. Chow and his helper are driving across the country to deliver prize-winning pumpkins. Most of the highways he plans to take have a speed limit of 55 miles per hour. Use this speed to solve the problems below. Use regrouping and place values when you multiply to solve each exercise.

1. How far would Mr. Chow travel in 8 hours?

______________________

2. If Mr. Chow drives from 6 A.M. to 6 P.M., how far would he travel?

______________________

3. Mr. Chow had to slow down to 45 miles per hour in a construction zone. How far would he travel in the construction zone for $2\frac{1}{2}$ hours?

______________________

4. If the speed limit on one highway is 65 miles per hour, how far could Mr. Chow travel in 5 hours?

______________________

5. How much farther would Mr. Chow travel in 5 hours driving 65 miles per hour than in 5 hours in a construction zone?

______________________

6. Mr. Chow drove through several states on his return trip to visit relatives. He drove for 3 hours in a construction zone, 8 hours driving 55 miles per hour, and 2 hours driving 65 miles per hour. How many miles did he drive altogether?

______________________

7. Mr. Chow took his prize-winning pumpkin to the state fair. He drove 112.5 miles at 45 miles per hour, 357.5 miles at 55 miles per hour, and 195 miles at 65 miles per hour. How many hours did he spend driving altogether?

______________________

Name ______________________________



1. A delivery truck travels 346 miles each day for 5 days. What is the total number of miles the truck travels?

   **A** 1,500 miles

   **B** 1,523 miles

   **C** 1,700 miles

   **D** 1,730 miles

2. A group of 106 campers sits in a big circle. The camp leader tells the campers to say "hello" to the person sitting next to them on each side. What is the total number of times the campers say "hello"?

   **A** 226

   **B** 212

   **C** 206

   **D** 202

3. If each shaded square is $\frac{1}{10}$, what number does the model show?

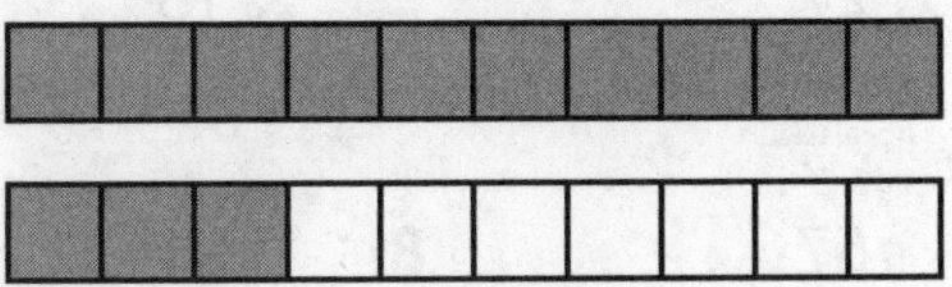

   **A** 0.13

   **B** 1.3

   **C** 3.7

   **D** 13.7

4. One cubic foot of concrete weighs about 145 pounds. What is the weight of 9 cubic feet of concrete?

______________________________

5. The graph shows the number of states the students in Mr. Robb's class have visited.

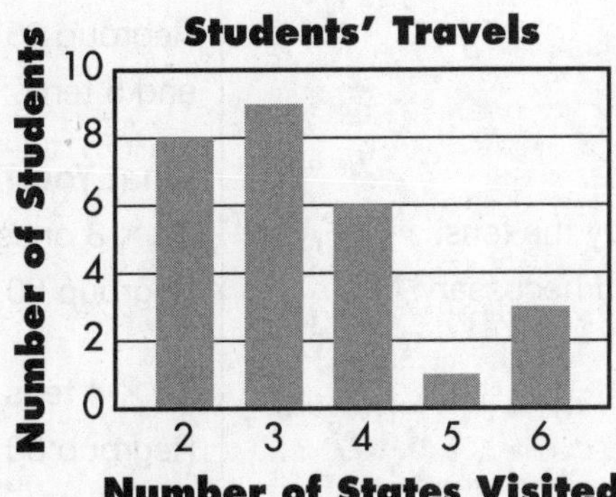


How many students have visited at least 4 states?

______________________________

6. Write this number in word form: 40.302

______________________________

______________________________



 

Name ______________________



# Multiplying 2-Digit by 2-Digit Numbers

Find 43 × 26.

| | What You Think | What You Write |
|---|---|---|
| **Step 1:**<br>Multiply by the ones.<br>Regroup if necessary. | 6 × 3 ones = 18 ones<br>Regroup 18 ones as 1 ten and 8 ones.<br><br>6 × 4 tens = 24 tens<br>24 tens + 1 ten = 25 tens<br>Regroup 25 tens as 2 hundreds and 5 tens. | 1<br>43<br>× 26<br>258 |
| **Step 2:**<br>Multiply by the tens.<br>Regroup if necessary. | 20 × 3 ones = 60 ones<br>Regroup 60 ones as 6 tens.<br><br>20 × 4 tens = 80 tens<br>Regroup 80 tens as 8 hundreds. | 1<br>43<br>× 26<br>258<br>860 |
| **Step 3:**<br>Add the partial products. | 6 × 43 = 258<br>20 × 43 = 860 | 1<br>43<br>× 26<br>258 ← partial products<br>+ 860 ←<br>1,118 |

Find the product.

**1.** 38 × 12

**2.** 64 × 33

**3.** 49 × 27

**4.** 85 × 15

**5.** 26 × 21

**6.** 73 × 19

**7.** 57 × 28

**8.** 91 × 86

**9.** In the problem 62 × 45, what are the partial products?

______________________________



 

Name ______________________________



# Multiplying 2-Digit by 2-Digit Numbers

Find each product. Estimate to check that your answer is reasonable.

**1.** $56 \times 34$

**2.** $45 \times 76$

**3.** $35 \times 15$

**4.** $47 \times 94$

**5.** $64 \times 51$

**6.** $47 \times 30$

**7.** $56 \times 19$

**8.** $92 \times 49$

**9.** To pay for a sofa, Maddie made a payment of 64 dollars each month for one year. How much did the sofa cost ? ______________

**10.** Katie is in charge of buying juice for the teachers' breakfast party. If one teacher will drink between 18 and 22 ounces of juice, and there are 32 teachers, which is the best estimate for the amount of juice Katie should buy?

**A** about 200 ounces
**B** about 400 ounces
**C** about 600 ounces
**D** about 800 ounces

**11.** Is 7,849 a reasonable answer for $49 \times 49$? Why or why not?

______________________________

______________________________

______________________________



 

Name ______________________



# Jackson's Bakery

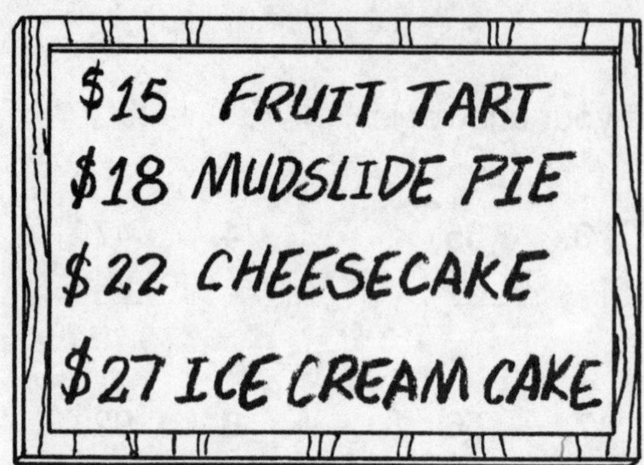


1. Jackson's Bakery sold 29 cheesecakes in one day. How much money did Jackson's Bakery make in one day from cheesecakes?

______________________

2. Jackson's Bakery sold 15 ice cream cakes and 31 fruit tarts in one weekend. How much money did Jackson's Bakery make in one weekend from ice cream cakes and fruit tarts?

______________________

3. The new pastry chef at Jackson's Bakery specializes in sheet cakes for parties. She sold 17 small, 11 medium, and 20 large sheet cakes in one week. How much money did Jackson's Bakery make in one week from sheet cakes?

______________________

4. How many people would all of the sheet cakes sold in problem 3 feed?

______________________

Name ______________________

Daily Common Core Review
**3-8**

**1.** A parking lot has 68 rows with 24 parking spaces in each row. What is the total number of parking spaces?

**A** 1,632

**B** 1,502

**C** 408

**D** 272

**2.** Sharla and Tim each build a brick wall using the same-size bricks. Sharla's wall is 28 rows with 14 bricks each. Tim's wall is 14 rows with 28 bricks each. Which statement about Sharla's wall is correct?

**A** It has more bricks than Tim's wall.

**B** It has fewer bricks than Tim's wall.

**C** It has the same number of bricks as Tim's wall.

**D** It has twice as many bricks as Tim's wall.

**3.** The ABC Company has 67,590 workers. The Smith Company has 5,348,299 workers. How many workers do the two companies have in all?

**A** 5,305,789

**B** 5,415,889

**C** 11,097,299

**D** 12,107,299

**4.** The sports field at Patton Elementary School is shaped like a rectangle. The field is 72 yards long and 46 yards wide. What is the area of the field in square yards?

______________________

______________________

**5.** Gina is making a square tablecloth.

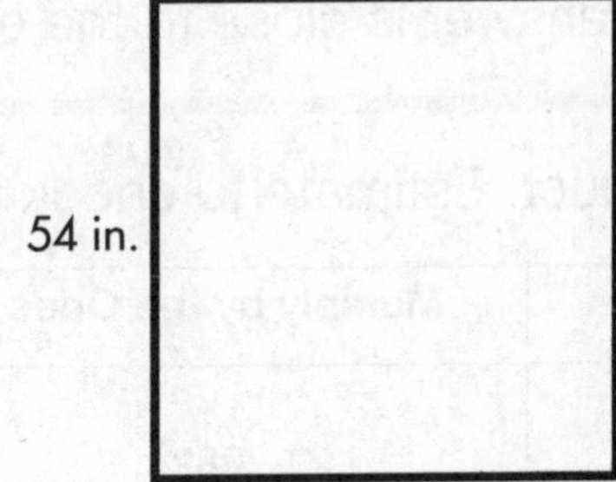


What is the least number of inches of trim Gina will need to go all the way around the edge of the tablecloth?

______________________

**6.** Round to the place of the underlined digit: 8,491,0<u>3</u>8,205.

______________________



 

Name ____________________

Reteaching **3-8**

# Multiplying Greater Numbers

Find 128 × 23. Estimate: 100 × 20 = 2,000

| | Step 1 | Step 2 | Step 3 |
|---|---|---|---|
| | Multiply by the ones. Regroup as needed. | Multiply by the tens. Regroup as needed. | Add the products. |
| 128<br>× 23<br>384<br>+ 2,560<br>2,944 | 2<br>128<br>× 3<br>384 | 1<br>128<br>× 20<br>2,560 | |

Because the answer is close to the estimate, the answer is reasonable.

Find the product. Estimate to check if your answer is reasonable.

| Problem | Multiply by the Ones | Multiply by the Tens | Add the Products |
|---|---|---|---|
| **1.** 282<br>× 19<br>2,538<br>+ | 7 1<br>282<br>× 9<br>2,538 | 282<br>× 10 | |
| **2.** 538<br>× 46 | | | |

**3.** Is 2,750 a reasonable answer for 917 × 33? Explain.

____________________

____________________

____________________

Name ______________________

Practice
**3-8**

# Multiplying Greater Numbers

Find each product. Estimate to check that your answer is reasonable.

**1.** $556 \times 34$

**2.** $234 \times 75$

**3.** $395 \times 76$

**4.** $483 \times 57$

**5.** $628 \times 33$

**6.** $154 \times 35$

**7.** $643 \times 49$

**8.** $536 \times 94$

**9.** In a class of 24 students, 13 students sold over 150 raffle tickets each, and the rest of the class sold about 60 raffle tickets each. The class goal was to sell 2,000 tickets. Did they reach their goal? Explain.

______________________

______________________

______________________

**10.** Player A's longest home run distance is 484 ft. If Player A hits 45 home runs at his longest distance, what would the total distance be? ____________

**11.** Player B's longest home run distance is 500 ft. There are 5,280 ft in 1 mi. How many home runs would Player B need to hit at his longest distance for the total to be greater than 1 mi? ____________

**12.** Which equation shows how you can find the number of minutes in one year?

**A** $60 \times 24 \times 365$
**B** $60 \times 60 \times 24$
**C** $60 \times 365$
**D** $60 \times 60 \times 365$

**13.** Write a real-world problem where you would have to multiply 120 and 75.

______________________

Name ______________________________

Enrichment
**3-8**

# School Fair

The fifth-grade students at River Dell Middle School are trying to set records during the annual school fair. Help them tally the totals for the events below.

1. The students put together 12 jigsaw puzzles. Each puzzle had 345 pieces. How many puzzle pieces did they put together in all?

   ______________________________

2. The students made a gigantic s'more that all of the fairgoers enjoyed. They used 27 bags of marshmallows. Each bag had 198 marshmallows. How many marshmallows did the students use?

   ______________________________

3. The students used 35 boxes of graham crackers to make the s'more. Each box had 208 graham crackers. How many graham crackers did the students use?

   ______________________________

4. The students used 19 cases of chocolate to make the s'more. Each case had 154 bars of chocolate. How many chocolate bars did the students use?

   ______________________________

5. The students painted an enormous mural. They used 21 cartons of paint. Each carton had 307 tubes of paint. How many tubes of paint did the students use?

   ______________________________

6. The students made a tub of lemonade for the fairgoers. They used 46 cases of lemons. Each case held 105 lemons. How many lemons did the students use?

   ______________________________



 

Name ____________________



1. Which answer is equal to $3^4$?

A $6^2$

B $4^3$

C $8^2$

D $9^2$

2. If 2,347,895 is rounded to the nearest hundred thousand, which of the following numbers will it be?

A 2,350,000

B 2,348,000

C 2,300,000

D 2,000,000

3. Delfina is moving to a new house, and she is packing some books in a box that measures 12 inches tall by 12 inches wide by 12 inches deep. Write the measurements of the box in exponential notation, in standard form, and in expanded form.

____________________

____________________

____________________

____________________

4. Write the following numbers in exponential notation and standard form.

$5 \times 5 \times 5 \times 5 \times 5 \times 5$

$8 \times 8 \times 8 \times 8$

____________________

____________________



 

Name ___________________________

Reteaching **3-9**

# Problem Solving: Draw a Picture and Write an Equation

A hardware store ordered 9 packs of screws from a supplier. Each pack contains 150 screws. How many screws did the store order?

**Read and Understand**

What do you know?

The store ordered nine packs of screws.

Each pack contained 150 screws.

What are you trying to find?

The total number of screws ordered

**Plan and Solve**

Draw a picture of what you know.



Write an equation.

Let $x$ = the total number of screws.

$9 \times 150 = x$

Multiply.

$$\begin{array}{r} {}^{4}\phantom{00} \\ 150 \\ \times\ 9 \\ \hline 1{,}350 \end{array}$$

The store ordered 1,350 screws.

**Look Back and Check**

Is your answer reasonable?

Yes, $150 \times 10 = 1{,}500$.

A state aquarium has display tanks that each contains 75 fish. Three of these tanks are at the entrance. How many fish are on display at the entrance?

Draw a picture. Write an equation. Solve.

___________________________



 

Name ______________________

Practice
3-9

# Problem Solving: Draw a Picture and Write an Equation

Draw a picture and write an equation. Then solve.

1. When Mary was born, she weighed 8 pounds. When she was 10 years old, she weighed 10 times as much. How much did she weigh when she was 10 years old?

2. Sandi is 13 years old. Karla is 3 times Sandi's age. How old is Karla?

3. Hwong can fit 12 packets of coffee in a small box and 50 packets of coffee in a large box. Hwong has 10 small boxes and would like to reorganize them into large boxes. Which boxes should he use? Explain.

4. Daniel has 12 tennis balls. Manuel has twice as many tennis balls as Daniel. Kendra has twice as many balls as Manuel. How many tennis balls do they have in all?

   **A** 24 **B** 36 **C** 84 **D** 96

5. William travels only on Saturdays and Sundays and has flown 400 miles this month. Jason travels every weekday and has flown 500 miles this month. Who travels more miles *per day* for this month? Explain.



 

Name ______________________

Enrichment
**3-9**

# Budgeting

Frank needs to go grocery shopping. He wants to buy items from each of the four food groups shown. He has a budget of $10.00. Using the chart at the right, help Frank decide what he should buy.

| Fruits and Vegetables | | Grains | |
|---|---|---|---|
| Strawberries | $2.99 | Bread | $1.99 |
| Apples | $3.99 | Bagels | $3.49 |
| Pears | $1.69 | Cereal | $4.29 |
| **Dairy** | | **Meat and Fish** | |
| Milk | $3.29 | Turkey | $2.99 |
| Cheese | $1.89 | Hamburger | $2.99 |
| Yogurt | $0.79 | Tuna | $1.89 |

**1.** What is the most Frank can spend on each food group if he spends the same on each?

______________________

**2.** If Frank chooses 2 dairy items, can he still buy something from each of the other 3 groups?

______________________

______________________

______________________

**3.** Show one possible menu for Frank. Tell how much he spent.

______________________

______________________

**4.** Frank remembers that he has fruit already. Show a possible menu for the remaining groups. Tell how much he spent.

______________________

______________________

Name ______________________

Daily Common Core Review
**4-1**

**1.** Steve uses 6 balls of yarn to knit a sweater. Knitting a blanket takes 15 times as many balls of yarn. Which equation can Steve use to find b, the number of balls of yarn he needs to knit a blanket?

**A** $6 + 15 = b$

**B** $6 \times 15 = b$

**C** $6 + b = 15$

**D** $6 \times b = 15$

**2.** Meg buys 12 bags of sunflower seeds. Each bag has 58 seeds. How many seeds does Meg buy?

**A** 696

**B** 686

**C** 174

**D** 116

**3.** After waking up, it takes Cheyenne 35 minutes to get ready to leave for school. She takes 20 minutes to walk to school. If Cheyenne wakes up at 7:15 A.M., at what time does she arrive at school?

**A** 7:40 A.M.

**B** 7:55 A.M.

**C** 8:00 A.M.

**D** 8:10 A.M.

**4.** A building has 8 same-sized apartments. The area of 1 apartment is 725 square feet. Let *t* be the total area of the 8 apartments.

**a.** Draw a picture to describe *t*.

**b.** Write an equation that you could use to find *t*.

______________________

**c.** What is the value of *t*?

______________________

**5.** For the 2004–05 school year, the state of Texas spent about thirty-eight billion dollars on education. Write this amount of money in standard form.

______________________

**6.** Last year, Handy Hardware Store sold 45,078 bolts and 5,011,542 nails. How many more nails did the store sell than bolts?

______________________



 

Name ____________________



# Dividing Multiples of 10 and 100

You can use math facts and patterns to help you divide mentally.

What is 480 ÷ 6?

You already know that 48 ÷ 6 = 8.

480 has one more zero than 48, so place one more zero in the quotient.

48<u>0</u> ÷ 6 = 8<u>0</u>.

What is 60,000 ÷ 6?

60 ÷ 6 = 10

60,000 has three more zeros than 60, so place three zeros in the quotient.

60,<u>000</u> ÷ 6 = 10,<u>000</u>.

Find each quotient. Use mental math.

**1.** 32 ÷ 8 = ______ **2.** 320 ÷ 8 = ______ **3.** 3,200 ÷ 8 = ______ **4.** 32,000 ÷ 8 = ______

**5.** 56 ÷ 7 = ______ **6.** 560 ÷ 7 = ______ **7.** 5,600 ÷ 7 = ______ **8.** 56,000 ÷ 7 = ______

**9.** 15 ÷ 3 = ______ **10.** 150 ÷ 3 = ______ **11.** 1,500 ÷ 3 = ______ **12.** 15,000 ÷ 3 = ______

**13. Writing To Explain** Explain how dividing 720 by 9 is like dividing 72 by 9.

____________________________________________

____________________________________________

Arlo has a newspaper delivery job. He wants to wrap each of his newspapers in a plastic bag to protect them from the rain. The newspapers are in bundles.

| Arlo's Newspaper Delivery | |
|---|---|
| Number of bundles | 12 |
| Number of newspapers per bundle | 9 |

Use mental math to answer the following questions.

**14.** How many bags will he use for 5 bundles? ______

**15.** How many bags will he use for 7 bundles? ______

**16.** How many bags will he use for all 12 bundles? ______



 

Name ______________________

Practice
**4-1**

# Dividing Multiples of 10 and 100

Use mental math to find each quotient.

**1.** $27 \div 9 =$ ________ **2.** $270 \div 9 =$ ________ **3.** $2{,}700 \div 9 =$ ________

**4.** $24 \div 4 =$ ________ **5.** $240 \div 4 =$ ________ **6.** $2{,}400 \div 4 =$ ________

**7.** $720 \div 9 =$ ________ **8.** $140 \div 7 =$ ________ **9.** $2{,}100 \div 3 =$ ________

**10.** If a bike race covers 120 mi over 6 days and the cyclists ride the same distance each day, how many miles does each cyclist ride each day? ________

Use mental math to answer the following questions.

| Dealership Vehicle Storage | |
|---|---|
| Sections of vehicles | 4 |
| Vehicles for sale | 1,200 |
| Rows per section | 10 |

**11.** If the vehicles are divided evenly between the sections, how many vehicles are in each section?

________

**12.** If the vehicles are divided evenly between the rows in each section, how many vehicles are in each row? ________

**13.** If $160{,}000 \div n = 4$, find $n$. ________

**14.** Find $32{,}000 \div 8$ mentally.

**A** 4,000 **B** 400 **C** 40 **D** 4

**15.** Solve the equation $n \times 50 = 5{,}000$. Explain your solution.

________



 

Name ______________________________



# Fun and Relaxation

1. Ten friends won the grand prize in the raffle. They won 2,000 music CDs. Use mental math to find out how many CDs each of the friends receives if they divide the prize equally.

   ______________________________

2. If Jasmine roller skates 280 miles in 7 weeks and skates the same distance each week, how many miles does she skate each week?

   ______________________________

3. Four sisters are going on a camping trip. They need to divide up their supplies equally to carry in their backpacks. If they want to bring along 120 energy bars, how many will each sister carry?

   ______________________________

4. The Green family has a movie rental plan of 900 movies per year. Mr. and Mrs. Green rent a certain number of movies, and their children Tyrone and Tina divide the remaining movies in half. How many movies can each of the children rent per year?

   ______________________________

**DVD Rentals**

| Name | Number of Movies |
|---|---|
| Mr. Green | 300 |
| Mrs. Green | 380 |
| Tyrone | |
| Tina | |

5. If Kevin writes 850 words in his blog from Monday through Friday, and he writes the same number of words each day, how many words does he write each day?

   ______________________________



 

Name ______________________________



1. **Mental Math** A school's Parent-Teacher Club raises $280 by washing cars. Each car wash costs $4. How many cars did the club wash?

   **A** 7

   **B** 70

   **C** 700

   **D** 7,000

2. In basketball, if a player makes a basket from behind a certain line, the basket is worth 3 points. Last year, a team made 392 of its 3-point baskets. How many points did the team earn last year from 3-point baskets?

   **A** 1,176

   **B** 1,086

   **C** 976

   **D** 395

3. Mr. Lopez buys shoes for his two children, Maria and Juan. Maria's shoes cost $28.35 with tax. Juan's shoes cost $30.97 with tax. How much did Mr. Lopez pay for Maria's and Juan's shoes?

   **A** $57.05

   **B** $58.22

   **C** $59.32

   **D** $68.05

4. **Mental Math** A flour mill produces the same amount of flour every hour. At the end of 8 hours, the mill has produced 48,000 pounds of flour. How many pounds of flour does the mill produce in 1 hour?

   ______________________________

5. In the year 2000, San Antonio, Texas, had a population of 1,144,646. What is this population rounded to the nearest hundred thousand?

   ______________________________

6. This thermometer shows the normal temperature of a healthy adult human.

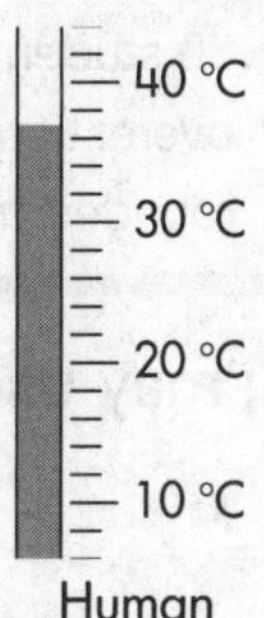


The temperature of a fish could be 19°C lower. Mark the fish's temperature on the thermometer below.

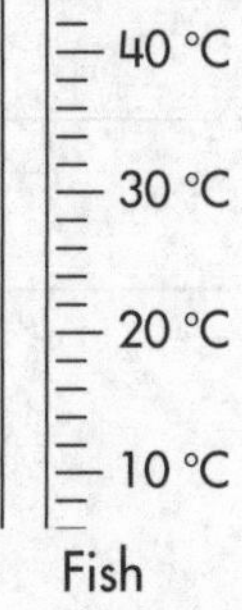




 

Name ____________________

Reteaching **4-2**

# Estimating Quotients

There are several ways to adjust whole numbers to estimate quotients.

Example:

There are 216 students. The school has 8 classrooms. How many students will be in each classroom?

Estimate $216 \div 8$.

**Rounding**

You can use rounding to estimate a quotient.

Round 216 to the nearest hundred.

In this case, 216 rounds to 200.

$200 \div 8 = 25$

25 students per room is an underestimate, because 216 was rounded down to 200.

**Compatible Numbers**

You can use compatible numbers to estimate a quotient.

Change 216 to a compatible number for 8.

Compatible numbers for 8 are numbers divisible by 8, such as 160, 240, and 320. Choose 240, because it is the closest compatible number to 216.

$240 \div 8 = 30$

30 students per class is an overestimate, because 216 was rounded up to 240.

**Multiplication**

You can use multiplication to estimate a quotient.

Think: 8 times what number is about 216?

$8 \times 25 = 200$

$8 \times 30 = 240$

216 is between 200 and 240. So a good estimate is a little more than 25 and a little less than 30 students per classroom.

Estimate each quotient. You may use any method.

**1.** $411 \div 2$ ____________________

**2.** $162 \div 4$ ____________________

**3. Estimation** If you estimate $342 \div 7$ by using $350 \div 7 = 50$, is 50 greater than or less than the exact answer? How did you decide? Is 50 an overestimate or an underestimate?

____________________

____________________



 

Name ______________________

Practice

4-2

# Estimating Quotients

Estimate each quotient. Tell which method you used.

1. 195 ÷ 4 __________ __________

2. 283 ÷ 5 __________ __________

3. 766 ÷ 8 __________ __________

4. 179 ÷ 2 __________ __________

5. $395.20 ÷ 5 __________ __________

6. $31.75 ÷ 8 __________ __________

7. $247.80 ÷ 5 __________ __________

8. If you use $63.00 ÷ 9 to estimate $62.59 ÷ 9, is $7.00 greater than or less than the exact answer? Explain.

__________

__________

9. A band played 3 concerts and earned a total of $321.00. The band earned about the same amount for each concert. Estimate how much the band earned each night.

__________

__________

10. At a department store, a woman's total was $284.00 for 7 items. Estimate the average cost per item.

11. Which is the closest estimate for 213 ÷ 4?

**A** 50 **B** 40 **C** 30 **D** 20

12. Explain how to estimate 524 ÷ 9.

__________

__________

Name ______________________

Enrichment
**4-2**

# Working Hard

1. Janelle earned $889 in 3 months for babysitting. If she was paid the same amount for each month, about how much did she earn per month?

______________________

2. Roberto is collecting stuffed toys to donate to 8 different charities. He wants to donate about the same amount to each charity. If Roberto collected 711 stuffed toys, about how many should he donate to each charity?

______________________

3. Julia is packing her paperweight collection into 7 boxes. She wants to put about the same number in each box. If Julia has 500 paperweights in her collection, about how many should she pack in each box?

______________________

4. Tony is testing a new type of sneaker for his mother's company. He will wear the sneaker for 6 days while he jogs on the beach for about the same distance each day. If Tony jogs 70 miles in 6 days, about how many miles does he jog each day?

______________________

5. Marissa is saving for a laptop computer. She deposited $391 into her bank account over 5 months. If she deposited the same amount into her account each month, about how much did she deposit each month?

______________________

6. The laptop computer that Marissa is saving for in Problem 5 costs $625. If she continues to deposit the same amount into her account each month, about how many more months will it take before she can purchase the computer?

______________________



 

Name ______________________________



1. **Estimation** Last summer, 137 kids signed up for swim lessons at City Pool. Each of the 7 swim teachers had about the same number of kids. About how many kids did each teacher have?

   **A** About 13

   **B** About 14

   **C** About 20

   **D** About 30

2. A scientist studies a sample that weighs 1 ounce, which is about 28 grams. About how many grams would be in a 48 ounce sample?

   **A** About 80 grams

   **B** About 600 grams

   **C** About 1,500 grams

   **D** About 2,800 grams

3. The state of Texas is 268,601 square miles in area. Rhode Island is 1,545 square miles. How much larger is Texas than Rhode Island?

   **A** 267,144 square miles

   **B** 267,056 square miles

   **C** 156,055 square miles

   **D** 114,101 square miles

4. **Estimation** A crew of house painters uses 814 gallons of paint to paint 9 buildings. They used about the same amount of paint for each. About how many gallons of paint did they use on each building?

   ______________________________

5. Logan puts a wallpaper border along the top edge of the 4 walls of a rectangular room. The room is 10 feet long and 12 feet wide. If there are no breaks in the border, how long is it?

   ______________________________

6. **Mental Math** There are 40,000 people at a football game. The seats are set up in 8 equal sections. How many people can sit in each section?

   ______________________________



 

Name ____________________



# Problem Solving: Reasonableness

After you solve a problem, check to see if your answer is reasonable. Also check that you answered the right question.

Example:
74 students are going to a special class dinner where they will be seated 8 to a table. Will 9 tables be enough?

| | |
|---|---|
| Reasonableness<br>$74 \div 8 = 9$ R2 | The answer is close to 9 tables. |
| Answering the right question | All students must have seats, so there must be one more table to hold the remaining 2 students, making 10 tables in all. |

Tell whether each answer is reasonable.

1. Kendra wants to paste 500 photographs into an album, 6 photos to a page. She figures that she will need about 100 pages.

____________________

____________________

____________________

____________________

2. Hwong has 39 muffins. If each of his guests will eat 2 muffins, Hwong figures that he can serve muffins to 19 guests.

____________________

3. Ivan has a piece of lumber 104 inches long. He is sawing it into 12-inch lengths to make fence posts. He says he can get about 9 fence posts out of the board.

____________________

____________________

____________________

____________________



 

Name ______________________

Practice
**4-3**

# Problem Solving: Reasonableness

Solve.

**1.** One tray holds eight sandwiches. If there are 30 sandwiches in all, how many trays are needed?

______________________

**2.** There are 53 students on a field trip. One chaperone is needed for every 6 students. How many chaperones are needed?

______________________

Mrs. Favicchio has 72 students in her science class. The table shows how many students can use each item of lab supplies she is ordering.

| Lab Supplies | |
|---|---|
| **Item** | **Number of Students** |
| Packet of pH paper | 10 |
| Case of test tubes | 5 |
| Case of petri dishes | 4 |

**3.** How many packets of pH paper does she need to order?

______________________

**4.** How many cases of test tubes does she need to order?

______________________

**5.** A loaf of banana bread serves 6 guests. There will be 47 guests attending the faculty breakfast. Which expression shows how many loaves are needed to serve them all?

**A** 47 divided by 6 is 7 R 5, so 7 loaves are needed.

**B** 47 divided by 6 is 7 R 5, so 8 loaves are needed.

**C** 47 plus 6 is 53, so 53 loaves are needed.

**D** 47 minus 6 is 41, so 41 loaves are needed.

**6. Writing To Explain** You are in line at an amusement park. You count 34 people in front of you. Each rollercoaster fits 11 people. How many rollercoasters must run before you can get on? Explain.

______________________

______________________



 

Name ____________________



# Place Your Orders

Mr. Christie has 37 students in his cake-decorating class. He is ordering supplies. The table shows how many students can use each item he buys.

| Cake Decorating Item | Number of Students it Will Serve |
|---|---|
| Box of pastry bags | 4 |
| Box of icing tips | 7 |
| Box of figurines | 3 |

**1.** Use the table to find out how many boxes of icing tips Mr. Christie needs to order.

____________________

**2.** Use the table to find out how many boxes of figurines Mr. Christie needs to order.

____________________

**3.** Ten more students joined the cake-decorating class. Use the table to find out how many boxes of pastry bags Mr. Christie needs to order.

____________________

**4.** Mr. Christie is ordering cartons of gingerbread house kits for 45 of his students. Each carton has enough kits for 6 students. How many cartons of gingerbread house kits does Mr. Christie need to order?

____________________

**5.** In the final class, each of Mr. Christie's 47 students will bake 3 cakes. All the cakes will be displayed in cases that can hold 15 cakes. How many cases will be needed to display all the cakes?

____________________



 

Name ______________________________

Daily Common Core Review

**4-4**

**1.** A baker makes 75 muffins. How many boxes of 4 muffins can the baker completely fill?

**A** 18

**B** 19

**C** 21

**D** 22

**2.** **Mental Math** Maria, Cho, and Kelly live in an apartment. They spend $180 for a new couch. If they split the cost equally, how much does each girl owe?

**A** $90

**B** $80

**C** $60

**D** $30

**3.** Ricky buys a big box of crayons. Inside the big box are 4 small boxes. Each small box holds the same number of crayons. Which do you need to know to find the total number of crayons Ricky buys?

**A** The width of a crayon

**B** The length of a crayon

**C** The cost of a small box of crayons

**D** How many crayons are in a small box

**4.** The Texas coast is 367 miles long. One day, 30 school groups pick up trash along the coast. Each group cleans up a different part of the coastline. Each group's part is the same length, a whole number of miles.

**a.** What is the greatest number of whole miles of coast that any one group could clean up?

______________________________

**b.** What is the length of the coast that NONE of the groups cleaned?

______________________________

**5.** A carpenter buys 144 boxes of nails. Each box has 36 nails. How many nails does the carpenter buy?

______________________________

**6.** Fill in the boxes to make the number sentences true.

$6 \times \square = \mathbf{48}$

$48 \div \square = \mathbf{8}$



 

Name ______________________________



# Connecting Models and Symbols

Divide 138 equally into 3 groups.

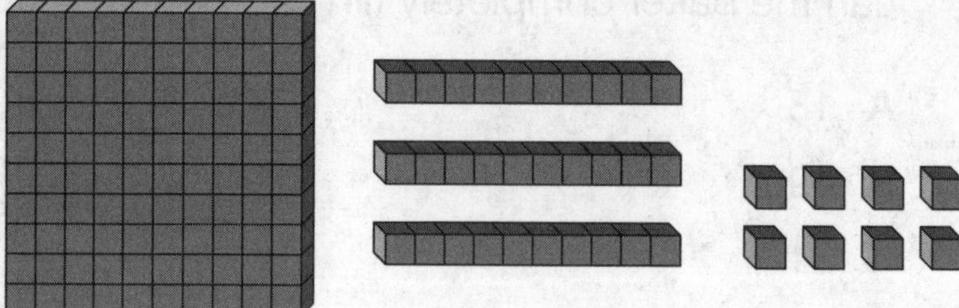

**Step 1:**
You can model 138 as 13 groups of 10 plus 8 ones.
Each group will get 4 groups of 10.
$40 \times 3 = 120$
$130 - 120 = 10$, so there is 1 group of 10 left.

**Step 2:**
There is 1 group of 10 plus 1 group of 8 ones left. You can model 18 as 18 ones.
$18 \div 3 = 6$, so each group will also get 6 ones. There is nothing left.

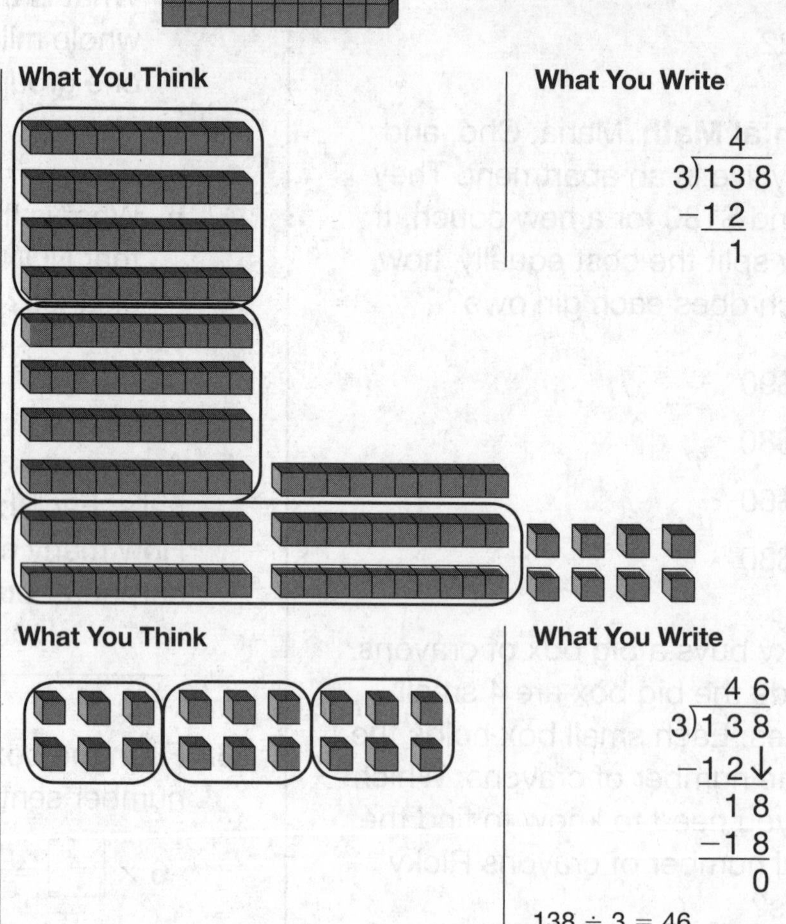


Use models to help you divide.

**1.** $4\overline{)76}$ **2.** $2\overline{)94}$ **3.** $5\overline{)130}$

**4.** $7\overline{)238}$ **5.** $6\overline{)426}$ **6.** $3\overline{)264}$

**7.** If $n \div 3 = 57$, what is the value of $n$?



 

Name ______________________



# Connecting Models and Symbols

After mowing lawns for one week, John put the money he earned on the table. There were four $100 bills, three $10 bills, and five $1 bills.

**1.** If John's brother borrowed one of the $100 bills and replaced it with ten $10 bills,

**a.** how many $100 bills would there be? ______________

**b.** how many $10 bills would there be? ______________

**2.** If John needed to divide the money evenly with two other workers, how much would each person receive? ______________

**3.** If John needed to divide the money evenly with four other workers, how much would each person receive? ______________

Complete each division problem. You may use play money or draw diagrams to help.

**4.**

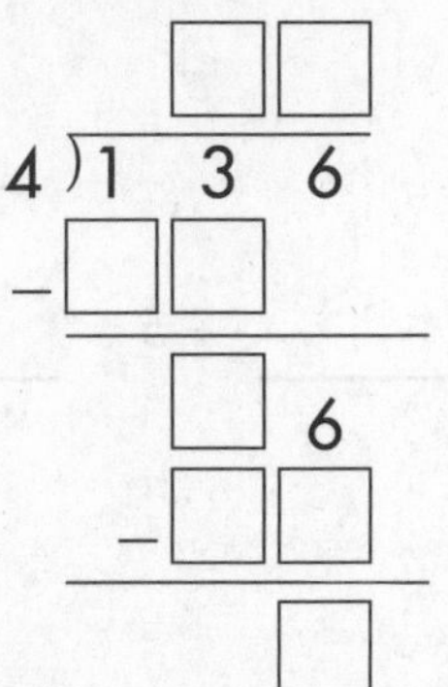

**5.**

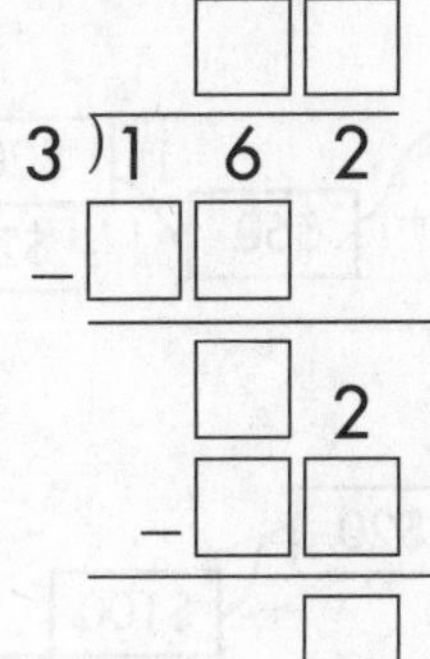

**6.** If $644.00 is divided equally among 7 people, how much will each person receive?

**A** $82.00 **B** $92.00 **C** $93.00 **D** $103.00

**7. Writing To Explain** Write a story problem using two $100 bills, nine $10 bills, and seven $1 bills.

______________________________________________

______________________________________________

______________________________________________

______________________________________________



 

Name ______________________

Enrichment
**4-4**

# Follow the Money Trail

Each trail below has money that you collect as you walk. At the end of each trail, the total amount of money is divided by a divisor. You receive the quotient.

**1.** $100 + $10 + $5 + $5 = ________ ÷ 2 = ________

**2.** 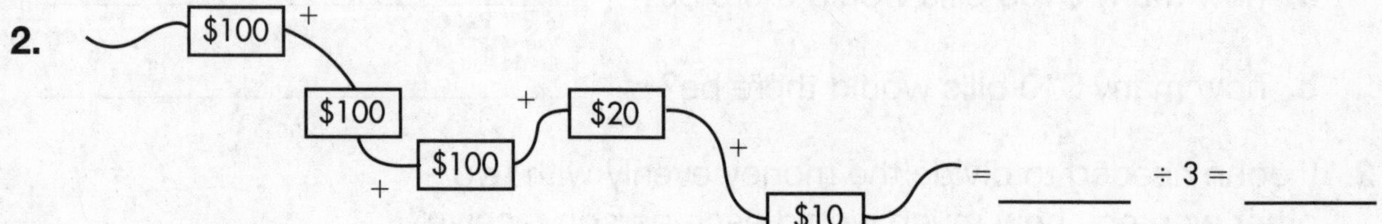

= ________ ÷ 3 = ________

**3.** 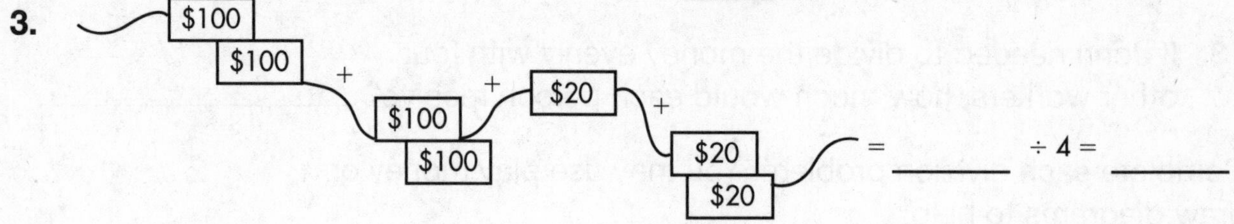

= ________ ÷ 4 = ________

**4.** 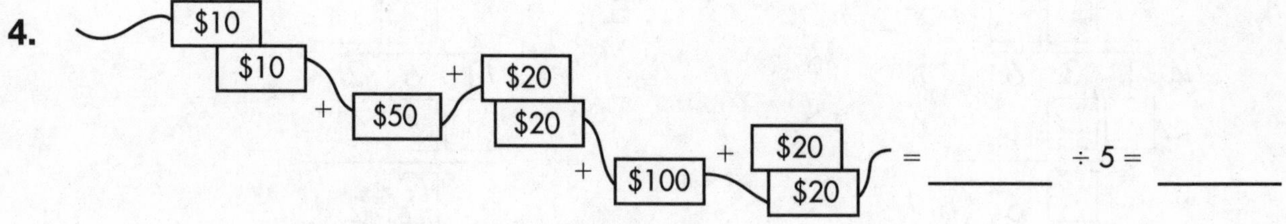

= ________ ÷ 5 = ________

**5.** $50 + $20 + $100 $100 + $100 $100 + $10 = ________ ÷ 6 = ________

**6.** $100 $100 + $50 $50 + $100 + $20 $20 + $50 = ________ ÷ 7 = ________



 

Name ____________________

Daily Common Core Review

**4-5**

**1.** The 4 businesses in a shopping center each pay an equal share of the center's electric bill. This month, they used 852 kilowatt-hours of electricity. How many kilowatt-hours must each business pay for?

**A** 210 kilowatt-hours

**B** 213 kilowatt-hours

**C** 240 kilowatt-hours

**D** 243 kilowatt-hours

**2.** **Estimation** Dakota has 416 baseball cards in 7 boxes. Each box has about the same number of cards. About how many cards are in each box?

**A** 80

**B** 60

**C** 50

**D** 40

**3.** D'Andre is 13 years old. How many days old is D'Andre? (Include 3 leap days.)

**A** 1,350

**B** 4,635

**C** 4,648

**D** 4,748

**4.** There are 6 salespeople at Good Folks Used Car Lot. Last year, they each sold the same number of cars. Together, they sold 534 cars. How many cars did each salesperson sell?

______________________

**5.** The table shows the area of the four oceans.

| Ocean | Area (square kilometers) |
|---|---|
| Arctic | 14,056,000 |
| Atlantic | 76,762,000 |
| Indian | 68,556,000 |
| Pacific | 155,557,000 |

List the oceans in order from greatest area to least area.

______________________

______________________

**6.** Does the shape below have any lines of symmetry? If so, draw each line of symmetry. If not, write *no lines of symmetry*.

______________________



 

Name ______________________________



# Dividing by 1-Digit Divisors

Find 362 ÷ 5.

| Step 1: To decide where to place the first digit in the quotient, compare the first digit of the dividend with the divisor. | Step 2: Divide the tens. Use multiplication facts and compatible numbers. Think $5 \times ? = 35$. | Step 3: Divide the ones. Use multiplication facts and compatible numbers. Think $5 \times ? = 10$. | Step 4: Check by multiplying. $5 \times 72 = 360$ $360 + 2 = 362$ |
|---|---|---|---|
| $3 < 5$, so the first digit in the quotient will not go in the hundreds place. | Write 7 in the tens place of the quotient. Multiply. $5 \times 7 = 35$ | Write 2 in the ones place of the quotient. Multiply. $5 \times 2 = 10$ | |
| Now, compare the first two digits of the dividend with the divisor. | $\begin{array}{r} 7 \\ 5\overline{)36} \\ -35 \\ 1 \end{array}$ | $\begin{array}{r} 72\text{R}2 \\ 5\overline{)362} \\ -35\downarrow \\ 12 \\ -10 \\ 2 \end{array}$ | |
| $36 > 5$, so the first digit in the quotient will go in the tens place. | Subtract. $36 - 35 = 1$ Compare. $1 < 5$ Bring down the ones. | Subtract. $12 - 10 = 2$ Compare. $2 < 5$ There are no more digits to bring down, so 2 is the remainder. | |

Divide. Check by multiplying.

**1.** $8\overline{)955}$ **2.** $7\overline{)249}$ **3.** $5\overline{)365}$

**4.** $8\overline{)448}$ **5.** $2\overline{)499}$ **6.** $6\overline{)396}$

**7.** How can you tell before you divide 425 by 9 that the first digit of the quotient is in the tens place?

______________________________



 

Name ______________________________

Practice
**4-5**

# Dividing by 1-Digit Divisors

Find each quotient.

**1.** $2\overline{)586}$ **2.** $3\overline{)565}$ **3.** $5\overline{)718}$ **4.** $4\overline{)599}$

**5.** $5\overline{)642}$ **6.** $6\overline{)354}$ **7.** $9\overline{)210}$ **8.** $8\overline{)927}$

The Paez family lives in Louisville, Kentucky, and has decided to take a road trip for their summer vacation.

**9.** How many miles will the Paez family drive each day if they decide to take 5 days to drive 865 mi to Dallas? ______________

**10.** The Paez family decides they want to drive 996 mi to Boston in 6 days. How many miles will they drive each day? ______________

**11.** If a staff of 9 people had to clean a hotel with 198 rooms, how many rooms would each person have to clean if they divided the rooms equally?

**A** 29 **B** 25 **C** 23 **D** 22

**12.** Explain how to check the quotient from a division problem.

______________________________

______________________________

______________________________



 

Name ______________________

Enrichment
**4-5**

# At the Amusement Park

The chart below shows in seconds how long certain rides at the amusement park take to complete a specific number of revolutions. In the exercises below, estimate first to find how long one revolution will take. Then find the actual time per revolution.

| Ride | Number of Revolutions | Time (seconds) |
|---|---|---|
| Ferris wheel | 5 | 515 |
| Roller coaster | 4 | 832 |
| Merry-go-round | 3 | 609 |
| Swiss slalom | 7 | 840 |

1. Ferris wheel ______________________

2. Roller coaster ______________________

3. Merry-go-round ______________________

4. Swiss slalom ______________________



 

Name ____________________



1. Ms. Sanchez buys boxes to pack up 169 books. Each box holds 9 books. How many boxes should Ms. Sanchez buy?

**A** 25

**B** 19

**C** 18

**D** 11

2. The tallest mountain measured from the bottom of the ocean is Mauna Kea, in Hawaii. Mauna Kea is 33,474 feet tall, but only 13,796 feet of its height is above sea level. How many feet of Mauna Kea are *below* sea level?

**A** 19,678 feet

**B** 20,322 feet

**C** 46,160 feet

**D** 47,270 feet

3. A flower shop sells vases of mixed flowers. Each vase includes 3 roses. If the shop uses 882 roses, how many vases of mixed flowers do they sell?

____________________

4. The average distance from the Sun to the planet Neptune is 2,795,080,000 miles. Write this distance in word form.

____________________

____________________

____________________

____________________

____________________

5. Julia rents an apartment that costs $845 each month. How much rent will she owe for a year?

____________________



 

Name ____________________



# Zeros in the Quotient

Find 816 ÷ 4.

**Step 1:** Compare the first digit of the dividend with the divisor. 8 > 4, so the first digit in the quotient will go in the hundreds place.

Divide the hundreds. Think 4 × ? = 8.

Write 2 in the hundreds place of the quotient. Multiply. 4 × 2 = 8

```
   2
4)81
 -8↓
  01
```

Subtract. 8 − 8 = 0

Compare. 0 < 4

Bring down the tens.

**Step 2:** Compare. 1 < 4

You cannot divide the tens, so place 0 in the tens place of the quotient.

Bring down the ones.

```
  20
4)816
 -8 ↓
  016
```

**Step 3:** Compare. 16 > 4

Divide the ones. Think 4 × ? = 16.

Write 4 in the ones place of the quotient.

Multiply. 4 × 4 = 16

Subtract. 16 − 16 = 0

Compare. 0 < 4

There are no more digits to bring down, so the problem is done.

```
  204
4)816
 -8
  016
 - 16
    0
```

**Step 4:** Check by multiplying.

4 × 204 = 816

Find each quotient. Check your answers by multiplying.

**1.** 8)640  **2.** 3)322  **3.** 4)908

**4.** 15)225  **5.** 6)624  **6.** 6)965

**7.** Is 593 ÷ 6 a little less than 10, a little more than 10, a little less than 100, or a little more than 100? Explain.

_______________________________________________

_______________________________________________



 

Name ____________________



# Zeros in the Quotient

Find each quotient. Check your answers by multiplying.

**1.** $490 \div 7 =$ ____________ **2.** $326 \div 3 =$ ____________

**3.** $916 \div 3 =$ ____________ **4.** $720 \div 2 =$ ____________

**5.** $2\overline{)941}$ **6.** $9\overline{)982}$ **7.** $7\overline{)740}$ **8.** $5\overline{)703}$

**9.** If there are 505 seats in an auditorium divided equally into 5 sections, how many seats are in each section? ____________

**10.** A book company publishes 749 copies of a novel and distributes them to 7 bookstores. If each bookstore were to receive the same number of copies, how many copies would be sent to each store? ____________

**11.** In one year, Dolores and Tom's four children saved $420 by recycling cans. When they divided the money equally, how much money did each child receive?

**A** $50 **B** $100 **C** $105 **D** $1,500

**12. Writing To Explain** Explain why estimating before you divide $624 \div 6$ helps you place the first digit in the quotient.

____________________

____________________

____________________

Name ______________________

Enrichment

**4-6**

# Is the Bridge Safe?

The Davis Construction Company follows certain rules for building safe bridges: The distance between the bridge's supports, called the *span*, must not be more than 100 ft. The chart at the right shows how to classify bridges as very safe, safe, or unsafe. Find the span length of each bridge below. Then tell whether the bridge is very safe, safe, or unsafe.

**Bridge Safety Ratings**

| Length of Span | Rating |
|---|---|
| 0 to 50 ft | very safe |
| 51 to 100 ft | safe |
| 101 ft or more | unsafe |

**1.** Length of bridge: 252 ft

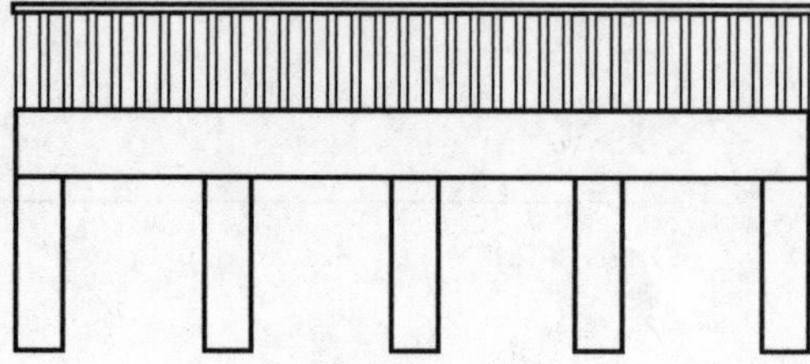

______________________________

**2.** Length of bridge: 336 ft

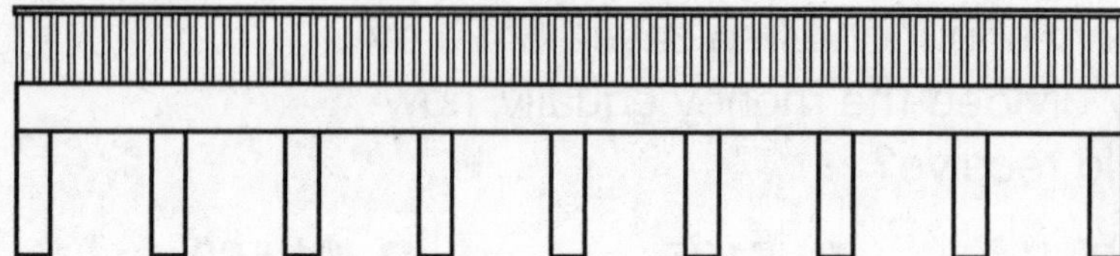

______________________________

**3.** Length of bridge: 266 ft

______________________________

Name ___

Daily Common Core Review

**4-7**

**1.** In a game, each player draws a number. If the number is prime, the player gets 5 points. The table shows four players and the numbers they draw.

**Game Results**

| Player | Number |
|---|---|
| Angel | 38 |
| Cory | 31 |
| Maria | 30 |
| Rachel | 35 |

Which player gets 5 points?

**A** Angel

**B** Cory

**C** Maria

**D** Rachel

**2.** A baker makes 84 loaves of bread, but she burns 4 of them. What fraction of the loaves does the baker burn?

**A** $\frac{1}{88}$

**B** $\frac{1}{80}$

**C** $\frac{1}{21}$

**D** $\frac{1}{20}$

**3.** Use a factor tree to find the prime factorization of 164.

___

**4.** Kevin buys a car. His car payment is $248 per month. After 55 payments, how much has Kevin paid?

___

**5.** The clock shows the time when Kelly left for school.

Kelly takes 15 minutes to walk to school. What time is it when she gets to school?

___



 

Name ______________________

Reteaching

**4-7**

# Problem Solving: Draw a Picture and Write an Equation

Mr. Rodriguez needs to store 10 test tubes in racks that hold 4 test tubes apiece. How many racks does he need?

Draw a picture.



Write an equation.

Let $r$ be the number of test-tube racks needed.

$10 \div 4 = r$

Solve the problem.

$r = 2 \text{ R } 2$

*Think: R 2 means that 2 test tubes are still left. Since they must be in a rack, one more rack is needed.*

Write the answer in a complete sentence.

Mr. Rodriguez will need three test-tube racks.

Mr. Rodriguez could also use racks that hold three test tubes or racks that hold five test tubes. Which racks should he use if he wants each rack completely filled? Explain.

______________________________________________

______________________________________________



 

Name ____________________



# Problem Solving: Draw a Picture and Write an Equation

Draw a picture and write an equation. Then solve.

**1.** Tommy paid $39 to fill up the gas tank in his car. If one gallon of gas costs $3, how many gallons of gas did Tommy put in?

______________________________

______________________________

**2.** To prepare for the brunch, Ivana needs to place 8 muffins in each basket. If she has 115 muffins, how many baskets will she need?

______________________________

______________________________

**3.** Write a real-world problem that you can solve by writing an equation. The answer to the problem must be 6.

______________________________

______________________________

**4.** The perimeter is the distance around an object. The perimeter of a square is 84 centimeters. What is the length of one side of the square?

**A** 75 cm **B** 42 cm **C** 21 cm **D** 14 cm

**5.** **Writing to Explain** A perfect score on a quiz is 100. Mrs. Frisoli gives students 1 point for putting their name on the paper. If there are only 9 questions on the quiz, how much is each question worth? Explain how you found your answer.

______________________________

______________________________

Name ______________________________



# Kayak Trip

Three sisters are going on a kayaking trip in the mountains. They will carry their supplies in their kayaks. If the sisters divide up the supplies below equally, how many of each item will each sister carry? How many will be left over?

**1.** 131 bottles of juice

______________________________

**2.** 295 energy bars

______________________________

**3.** 467 food packets

______________________________

**4.** 691 packs of matches

______________________________

**5.** The sisters plan to finish a trip of 351 miles in 13 days. How many miles will they paddle each day?

______________________________

**6.** The sisters took 868 photos on their kayak trip. If their photo albums each hold 75 photos, how many albums will they fill completely? How many photos will be in the last album?

______________________________

______________________________

**7.** The sisters used up 769 minutes on their cell phone plan. If their plan allows for 2,500 minutes and they divide up the remaining minutes, how many minutes will each sister have?

______________________________



 

Name ______________________________

**Daily Common Core Review**
**5-1**

**1.** When all the seats are filled, a Ferris wheel can take 72 people for a ride. There are 313 people waiting to ride the wheel. Which drawing represents the number of rides with all the seats filled?

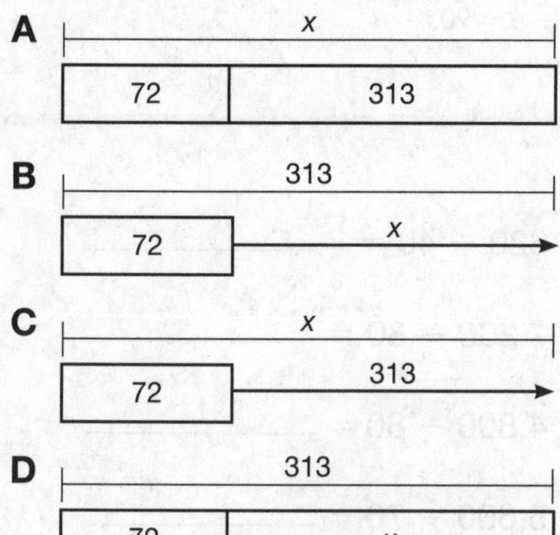


**2.** Last year, a bead store sold 104,002 glass beads and 47,357 wooden beads. How many more glass beads than wooden beads did the store sell?

**A** 54,755
**B** 56,645
**C** 67,645
**D** 67,755

**3.** A farmer has to pack 836 oranges into boxes. Each box holds 44 oranges. Let $b$ be the total number of boxes the farmer needs.

**a.** Draw a picture you can use to find $b$.

**b.** Write an equation to find $b$.

______________________________

**c.** How many boxes will the farmer need?

______________________________

**4.** The table shows the thickness of different brands of plastic bags.

| Brand | Thickness (centimeters) |
|---|---|
| Iron Sides | 0.023 |
| Mighty Hold | 0.003 |
| Steely Bags | 0.032 |
| Super XX | 0.004 |

List the brands of bags in order from thinnest to thickest.

______________________________

______________________________

______________________________



 

Name ______________________________



# Using Patterns to Divide

You can use basic facts and patterns to divide mentally.

| **Using basic facts** | **Using patterns** |
|---|---|
| What is 350 ÷ 70? | What is 5,400 ÷ 60? |
| Think: 350 ÷ 70 is the same as 35 tens ÷ 7 tens. | 5,400 ÷ 60 is the same as 540 ÷ 6. |
| 35 ÷ 7 = 5 | 54 ÷ 6 = 9, so 540 ÷ 6 = 90. |
| So, 350 ÷ 70 = 5. | So, 5,400 ÷ 60 = 90. |

Find each quotient. Use mental math.

**1.** 280 ÷ 70 = ______

**2.** 320 ÷ 40 = ______

**3.** 360 ÷ 60 = ______

**4.** 7,200 ÷ 80 = ______

**5.** 9,000 ÷ 30 = ______

**6.** 4,800 ÷ 80 = ______

**7.** 2,000 ÷ 40 = ______

**8.** 5,600 ÷ 70 = ______

**9.** How is dividing 250 by 50 the same as dividing 2,500 by 500?

______________________________

______________________________

______________________________

**10.** Explain how you can mentally determine that 35,000 ÷ 70 = 500.

______________________________

______________________________

______________________________

Name ______________________

Practice
5-1

# Using Patterns to Divide

In **1** through **4**, find each quotient. Use mental math.

**1.** 360 ÷ 40 = 36 tens ÷ 4 tens = ______________

**2.** 5,400 ÷ 90 = 540 tens ÷ 9 tens = ______________

**3.** 240 ÷ 30 = 24 tens ÷ 3 tens = ______________

**4.** 4,800 ÷ 10 = 480 tens ÷ 1 ten = ______________

Use mental math to answer the following questions.

**5.** If the vehicles are divided evenly among the sections, how many vehicles are in each section?

______________

| Dealership Vehicle Storage | |
|---|---|
| Sections of vehicles | 4 |
| Vehicles for sale | 1,200 |
| Rows per section | 10 |

**6.** If the vehicles are divided evenly among the rows in each section, how many vehicles are in each row?

______________

**7.** Suppose there are 297 students going on a field trip. If each schoolbus can carry 58 students, estimate the number of buses that will be needed to transport all the students.

______________

______________

**8.** If 1,600 ÷ $n$ = 4, what is the value of $n$?

**A** 40 **B** 400 **C** 4,000 **D** 40,000

**9.** Solve the equation $n \times 50 = 5{,}000$. Explain your solution.

______________

______________

Name ___________________________

Enrichment
5-1

# Move Those Zeros

Kerry uses a crane to lower zeros into the answers below. Cross off each zero after it has been used.

0 0 0 0 0 0

0 0 0 0 0 0

0 0 0 0 0

0 0 0

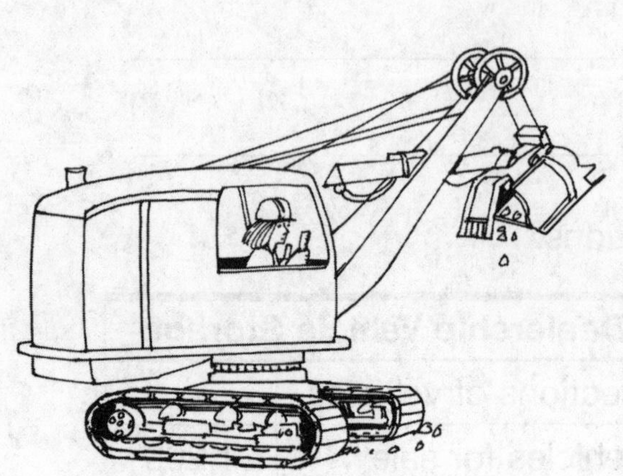

1. 24 ÷ 6 = ________
2. 560 ÷ 7 = 8________
3. 240 ÷ 6 = 4________
4. 56 ÷ 7 = ________
5. 2,400 ÷ 6 = 4________
6. 6,300 ÷ 9 = 7________
7. 24,000 ÷ 6 = 4________
8. 63 ÷ 9 = ________
9. 56,000 ÷ 7 = 8________
10. 63,000 ÷ 9 = 7________
11. 5,600 ÷ 7 = 8________
12. 630 ÷ 9 = 7________
13. How many zeros does Kerry have left over? ________
14. Write a division problem whose quotient has the same number of zeros that Kerry has left over.

_______________________________________________



 

Name ____________________



1. Carson School has 1,200 students. The principal organizes them into 40 teams for Field Day. If each team is the same size, how many people are on a team?

   **A** 30
   **B** 40
   **C** 116
   **D** 120

2. Look at the figure below made up of 1-unit cubes.

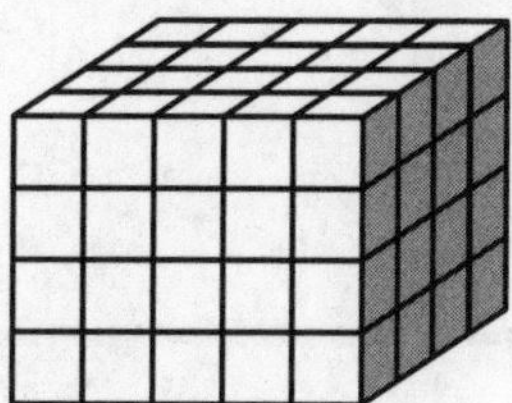

   Identify the three-dimensional shape.

   **A** Cone
   **B** Cylinder
   **C** Rectangular prism
   **D** Triangular prism

3. A service group earns $1,800 by recycling scrap metal. Each pound of scrap metal is worth $30. How many pounds of scrap metal did the group recycle?

   **A** 150
   **B** 60
   **C** 15
   **D** 6

4. Fill in the blanks to complete the table.

| | | |
|---|---|---|
| 400 ÷ 50 | = | 8 |
| 4,000 ÷ 50 | = | 80 |
| 40,000 ÷ 50 | = | ____ |
| 400,000 ÷ ____ | = | 8,000 |

5. Multiply.

$$\begin{array}{r} 416 \\ \times \ 34 \\ \hline \end{array}$$

   ____________

6. Emma buys a book and gives the clerk $13.00. How much did the book cost if her change is $0.33?

   ____________


 

Name ______________________________

# Estimating Quotients with 2-Digit Divisors

You can use compatible numbers to estimate a quotient.

Find 175 ÷ 32.

**Step 1:** Find compatible numbers for 175 and 32.

32 rounds to 30.

Think: 18 can be divided evenly by 3.

180 is close to 175 and 30 is close to 32.

180 and 30 are compatible numbers.

**Step 2:** Divide. Use patterns to help you, if possible.

Think: 180 ÷ 30 is the same as 18 tens ÷ 3 tens.

18 ÷ 3 = 6

So, 180 ÷ 30 = 6.

**Step 3:** Check for reasonableness.

6 × 30 = 180

So, a good estimate of 175 ÷ 32 is 6.

Estimate each quotient using compatible numbers.

1. 298 ÷ 25 ______________________

2. 5,391 ÷ 77 ______________________

3. 24,303 ÷ 12 ______________________

4. 276 ÷ 42 ______________________

5. 1,347 ÷ 54 ______________________

6. 5,564 ÷ 91 ______________________

At Elmer Elementary School, fifth-grade students are saving money for a summer trip to Washington, D.C.

| Student | Amount Saved |
|---|---|
| Percy | \$125 |
| Emily | \$ 80 |
| George | \$202 |
| James | \$ 41 |
| Bertha | \$159 |

7. The money Percy has saved is how many times as great as the money James has saved?

______________________________

______________________________

Name ______________________________



# Estimating Quotients with 2-Digit Divisors

In **1** through **4**, estimate the quotients using compatible numbers.

**1.** 566 ÷ 81 = __________ **2.** 453 ÷ 93 = __________

**3.** 1,423 ÷ 69 = __________ **4.** 8,631 ÷ 10 = __________

**5.** If you use $99.00 ÷ 11 to estimate $98.69 ÷ 11, is $9.00 greater than or less than the exact answer? Explain.

______________________________________________

______________________________________________

**6.** Suppose there are 19 students in a class. A teacher has 122 pencils and passes them out to the class. Estimate the number of pencils each student will receive. __________

**7.** At a department store, a package of 12 handkerchiefs costs $58.99. Estimate how much each handkerchief costs. __________

**8.** Which is the closest estimate for 2,130 ÷ 33?

**A** 7 **B** 17 **C** 70 **D** 700

**9.** Explain how to estimate 498 ÷ 12.

______________________________________________

______________________________________________

Name ______________________________

Enrichment
**5-2**

# They Have Clues!

Each person below has information for you. Use it to write the best estimate from the box for each exercise.

**Answer Box**

$50    5
7
30    $70

1. ____________

2. ____________

3. ____________

4. ____________

5. ____________

Name ____________________



1. Derrick is 13 inches taller than his little brother Cedric. Let $c$ be Cedric's height. Which gives Derrick's height?
   **A** $c + 13$
   **B** $c - 13$
   **C** $13 - c$
   **D** $13 \div c$

2. Mr. Alvarez buys a table, 4 chairs, and a china cabinet for his dining room. What fraction of these pieces of furniture are chairs?
   **A** $\frac{1}{4}$
   **B** $\frac{1}{3}$
   **C** $\frac{2}{3}$
   **D** $\frac{3}{4}$

3. Shante and Dawn go out for dinner. Shante's meal costs $12.45, and Dawn's meal costs $13.29. What is the cost of the two meals together?
   **A** $25.64
   **B** $25.74
   **C** $35.64
   **D** $36.74

4. Marnie's score on a test is $s$. Lisa's score is 7 points less than Marnie's score. Write an expression that gives Lisa's score.

   ____________________

5. A rocket travels 147,098,074 kilometers from Planet A to Planet B. Another rocket travels 152,097,701 kilometers from Planet A to Planet C. How much farther did the second rocket travel?

   ____________________



 

Name ___________________________



# Connecting Models and Symbols

Divide 345 by 15.

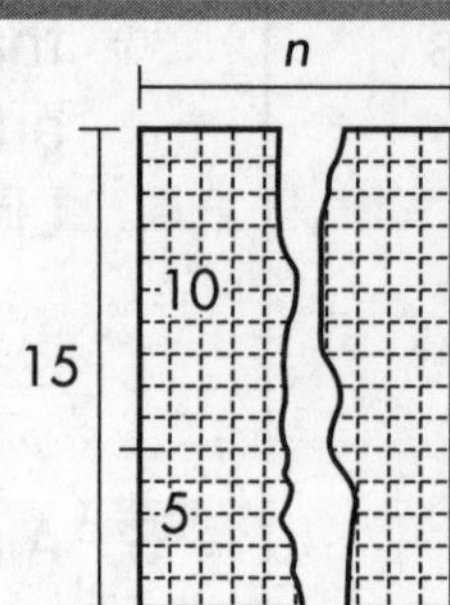


**Construct a model and write an equation**

$345 \div 15 = n$ or
$15 \times n = 345$

**Step 1:**
Divide the tens place.
15 goes in to 34 two times, so add two tens (20) to your area model.

**What You Think**

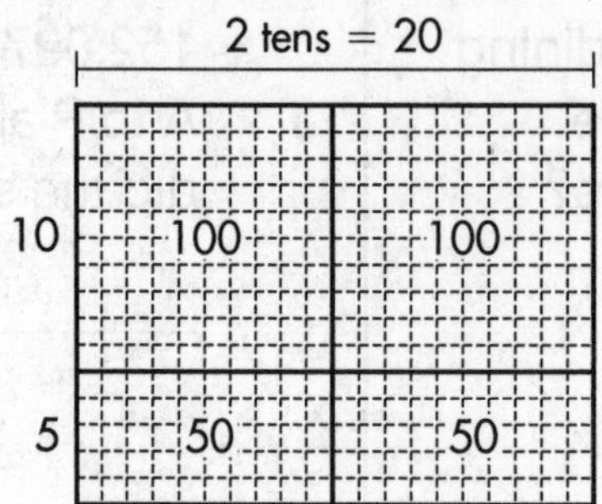


**What You Write**

$$\begin{array}{r} 2\phantom{5} \\ 15\overline{)345} \\ -30\phantom{5} \\ \hline 4\phantom{5} \end{array}$$

**Step 2:**
Divide the ones place.
15 goes into 45 three times, so add three ones to your area model.

**What You Think**

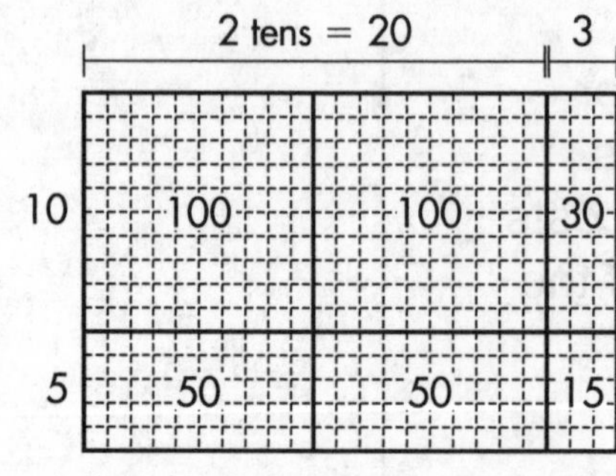


**What You Write**

$$\begin{array}{r} 23 \\ 15\overline{)345} \\ -30\downarrow \\ \hline 45 \\ -45 \\ \hline 0 \end{array}$$

$345 \div 15 = 23$

Use models to help you divide.

**1.** $12\overline{)228}$

**2.** $20\overline{)940}$

**3.** $15\overline{)390}$

Name ________________________________

Practice
5-3

# Connecting Models and Symbols

Use arrays, area models, or draw a diagram to help you solve.

**1.** 10)210 ________ **2.** 31)217 ________

**3.** 13)845 ________ **4.** 34)204 ________

**5.** 12)720 ________ **6.** 21)640 ________

Complete each division problem. You may use area models or draw pictures to help.

**7.**

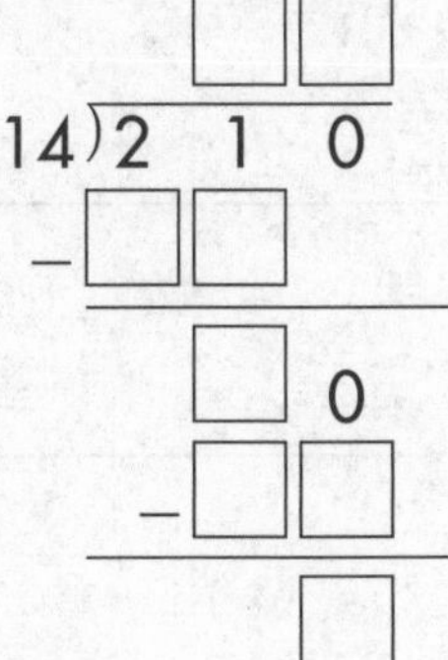

**8.**

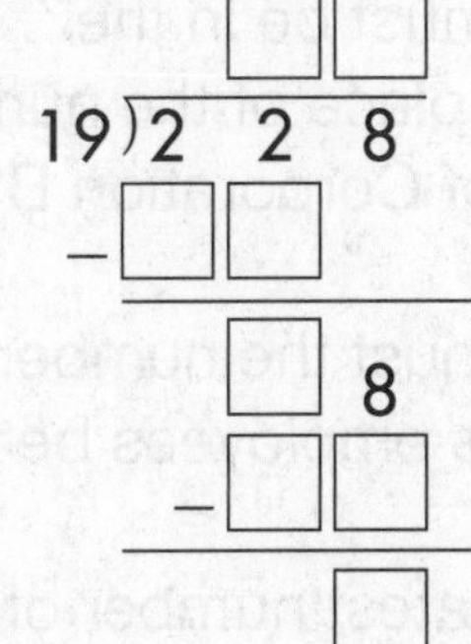

**9.** If $1000 is divided equally among twelve people, about how much will each person receive?

**A** $92.00 **B** $83.00 **C** $91.00 **D** $87.00

**10.** Write a story problem using a 3-digit dividend, a 2-digit divisor, and a 2-digit quotient. Draw a picture or use a model to help you illustrate the problem.

________________________________

________________________________

________________________________

________________________________

Name ______________________________



# Competing Corporations

Corporation A, Corporation B, and Corporation C are in the same city. Corporation A employs 330,000 people. Corporation B employs more than 320,000 people, but fewer than Corporation A employs. Corporation C has less than half the employees of Corporation A.

| Corporation A | Corporation B | Corporation C |
|---|---|---|
| Employees: 330,000 | Employees: $>$ 320,000 and $<$ Corporation A | Employees: $< \frac{1}{2}$ Corporation A |

1. What number must be in the ten-thousands place of the number of employees of Corporation B? ______________

2. What number must the number of Corporation C's employees be less than? ______________

3. What is the greatest number of employees Corporation C could have? ______________

4. What is the least number of additional people needed to make the number of employees of Corporation B greater than the number of employees of Corporation A? ______________

5. What is the sum of the greatest possible number of employees of all three corporations? ______________

6. What is the least number of employees who could be employed by Corporation B? ______________

7. Could Corporation C's employees be half of Corporation B's employees? ______________

Name ______________________________



**1.** Dora, Brent, Cara, and Andre go out for dinner. The bill is $32, plus $5.60 tax, and a $6.40 tip. Each person pays an equal share of the total cost. What is each person's share?

**A** $12
**B** $11
**C** $8
**D** $3

**2.** Mr. Lopez drives his car 12,000 miles each year for 5 years. What is the total number of miles Mr. Lopez drives?

**A** 6,000
**B** 60,000
**C** 600,000
**D** 6,000,000

**3.** A row in a parking lot is 214 yards wide. Each parking space is 2 yards wide. How many parking spaces will fit in one row?

**A** 170
**B** 120
**C** 107
**D** 102

**4.** A school principal orders 75 boxes of chalk. Each box has 12 sticks of chalk. The school has 23 teachers.
Does the principal have enough chalk to give each teacher 40 sticks? If yes, how many sticks are left over? If no, how many more sticks does the principal need?

______________________________

______________________________

______________________________

______________________________

______________________________

______________________________

**5.** A wire is 16.5 centimeters long. Lisa cuts 1.025 centimeters off one end of the wire. How long is the remaining wire?

______________________________

**6.** In 2005, the Houston Livestock Show and Rodeo had 1,740,095 visitors. What is the value of the digit 7 in this number of people?

______________________________

______________________________

Name



# Dividing by Multiples of 10

Find 623 ÷ 40.

**Step 1:** Estimate the quotient using compatible numbers, 600 ÷ 40 = 15. Then, divide the tens.

$$\begin{array}{r} 1 \\ 40\overline{)623} \\ -40 \\ \hline 22 \end{array}$$

Divide 62 ÷ 40
Multiply 1 × 40 = 40
Subtract 62 − 40 = 22
Compare 22 < 40

**Step 2:** Bring down the ones. Then, divide the ones.

$$\begin{array}{r} 15 \\ 40\overline{)623} \\ -40\downarrow \\ \hline 223 \\ -200 \\ \hline 23 \end{array}$$

Divide 223 ÷ 40
Multiply 5 × 40 = 200
Subtract 223 − 200 = 23

**Step 3:** Since 23 < 40, write 23 as the remainder in the quotient.

$$\begin{array}{r} 15\text{ R}23 \\ 40\overline{)623} \\ -40\downarrow \\ \hline 223 \\ -200 \\ \hline 23 \end{array}$$

Compare 23 < 40

Complete.

1. $60\overline{)288}$

2. $20\overline{)455}$

3. $80\overline{)866}$

4. $30\overline{)233}$

5. $50\overline{)498}$

6. Celia plans to pack her books in boxes when her family moves. Each box will hold 20 books. Celia has 97 books. How many boxes will she need to pack all her books?

______________________



 

Name ______________________________



# Dividing by Multiples of 10

In **1** through **6**, divide.

**1.** $20\overline{)467}$ ____________  **2.** $40\overline{)321}$ ____________

**3.** $80\overline{)813}$ ____________  **4.** $40\overline{)284}$ ____________

**5.** $90\overline{)648}$ ____________  **6.** $10\overline{)587}$ ____________

**7.** To drive from New York City, NY, to Los Angeles, CA, you must drive about 2,779 miles. If you drive 60 miles per hour , about how many hours would you spend driving? ____________

**8.** Suppose one bottle of paint can cover 20 tiles. You have 348 tiles. How many bottles of paint do you need to buy to cover all 348 tiles? Explain.

______________________________

______________________________

**9.** A group of 483 students is taking a field trip. One bus is needed for every 50 students. How many buses are needed?

______________________________

**10.** A decagon is a ten-sided figure. If a regular decagon has a perimeter of 114 centimeters, how long is each side of the figure?

**A** 11.4 cm **B** 14 cm **C** 114 cm **D** 124 cm

**11.** To figure out how many hours it will take to drive from his home to his cousin's house, a student divides 289 by 60 and estimates that it will take about 4.5 hours. Explain whether you think this is a reasonable estimate.

______________________________

______________________________

______________________________



 

Name ______________________________



# Blimp Rides

Blimps may float over public events. Use mental math and the numbers in the blimps to help answer **1** through **4**.

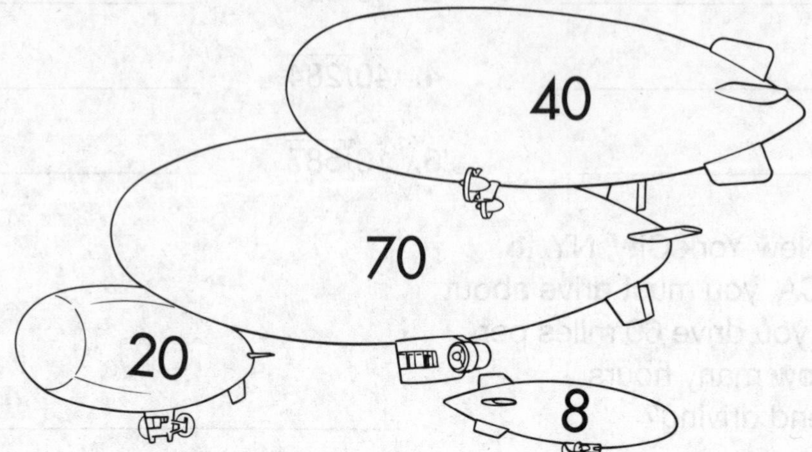


**1.** 400 people rode on 20 blimps. Each blimp carried the same number of people. How many people rode on each blimp? ______________

**2.** 320 people rode on 40 blimps. Each blimp carried the same number of people. How many people rode on each blimp? ______________

**3.** If 60 blimps each had 70 people on board, how many people would be riding on the blimps? ______________

**4.** If 25 blimps each had 40 people on board, how many people would be riding on the blimps? ______________

**5.** Use one of the numbers in the blimps and write an original division problem that can be solved by mental math.

______________________________

______________________________

______________________________

Name ______________________________



1. A computer can load 753 megabytes in 20 seconds. Which best describes the loading speed of the computer?

**A** Around 30 megabytes per second
**B** Close to 38 megabytes per second
**C** Nearly 40 megabytes per second
**D** More than 41 megabytes per second

2. The table shows the number of square feet painted by three house painters.

| Painter | Square Feet Painted | Days Worked |
|---|---|---|
| Martin | 719 | 2 |
| Juan | 825 | 3 |
| Christy | 836 | 3 |

Which best describes Christy's average painting speed?

**A** Almost 260 square feet per day
**B** Almost 270 square feet per day
**C** Almost 280 square feet per day
**D** Almost 290 square feet per day

3. A parking garage has 2 levels, and each level can accommodate 6 rows of 5 cars. Multiply to find out how many cars the garage can accommodate when filled to capacity.

**A** 90 cars
**B** 60 cars
**C** 30 cars
**D** 15 cars

4. List the painters in Question 2 in order from slowest to fastest average painting speed.

______________________________

______________________________

5. A business earns $45,692 in January and $70,359 in February. How much money did the business earn during these two months?

______________________________

6. The graph shows the number of votes for each person in a school election.

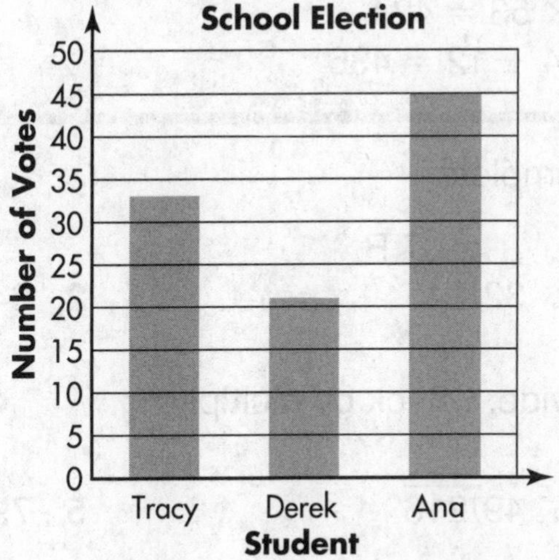


Which student won the election?

______________________________

Name ______________________



# 1-Digit Quotients

Find $436 \div 53$.

To find the answer, first estimate the quotient.

Think: $400 \div 50 = 8$ or $450 \div 50 = 9$

Try 9:

$$\begin{array}{r} 9 \\ 53\overline{)436} \\ \underline{-477} \end{array}$$

Write 9 in the ones place.
Multiply, $9 \times 53 = 477$.
$477 > 436$.
This estimate is too high.

Try 8:

$$\begin{array}{r} 8 \\ 53\overline{)436} \\ \underline{-424} \\ 12 \end{array}$$

Write 8 in the ones place.
Multiply, $8 \times 53 = 424$.
Subtract, $436 - 424 = 12$.
Compare, $12 < 53$. Write the remainder in the quotient.

$436 \div 53 = 8\text{ R}12$

Check:

$8 \times 53 = 424$

$424 + 12 = 436$

Complete.

**1.** $32\overline{)245}$ 7 R

**2.** $64\overline{)332}$ R12

**3.** $51\overline{)489}$ R

Divide. Check by multiplying.

**4.** $49\overline{)216}$

**5.** $79\overline{)698}$

**6.** $25\overline{)194}$

**7.** Explain how you know the answer to the problem below has an error.

$$\begin{array}{r} 2\text{ R}86 \\ 77\overline{)240} \\ \underline{-154} \\ 86 \end{array}$$

______________________________

______________________________



 

Name ______________________________



# 1-Digit Quotients

In **1** through **6**, find each quotient.

**1.** $37\overline{)120}$ **2.** $39\overline{)342}$ **3.** $62\overline{)338}$

**4.** $42\overline{)284}$ **5.** $82\overline{)599}$ **6.** $55\overline{)474}$

**7.** Solomon has $118. He wants to purchase concert tickets for himself and 5 friends. Each ticket costs $19. Does he have enough money? Explain.

______________________________

______________________________

**8.** Which problem will have the greater quotient, 376.0 ÷ 93 OR 376 ÷ 93.01? Explain how you know.

______________________________

______________________________

______________________________

**9.** Which is 458 ÷ 73?

**A** 5 R19 **B** 5 R20 **C** 6 R19 **D** 6 R20

**10.** A student solves the problem 354 ÷ 24. The student finds an answer of 13 R40. Explain how you can tell that the answer is incorrect just by looking at the remainder.

______________________________

______________________________

______________________________

Name ______________________________



# Orbiting Estimates

Mercury makes a complete orbit around the Sun in 88 days. Mars makes a complete orbit around the Sun in 687 days. In the exercises below, use compatible numbers and multiplication to make the estimates.

1. How many orbits around the Sun will Mercury make in 1,060 days? Show your work.

2. Now use a different operation to estimate for the same problem. Show your work.

3. Estimate the number of days it will take Mars to complete 12 orbits. Show your work.



 

Name ______________________

Daily Common Core Review

**5-6**

**1.** A librarian has 883 books to shelve. Each shelf holds 98 books. How many books will be left over after filling as many shelves as possible?

**A** 1

**B** 9

**C** 89

**D** 97

**2.** A marina has 16 docks. Each dock has room for the same number of boats. When 101 boats sail in, they fill all the docks, with 5 boats left over. How many boats are in each dock?

**A** 21

**B** 11

**C** 6

**D** 5

**3.** Jordan hikes $1\frac{1}{2}$ miles along a nature trail. Which point best represents $1\frac{1}{2}$ on the number line?

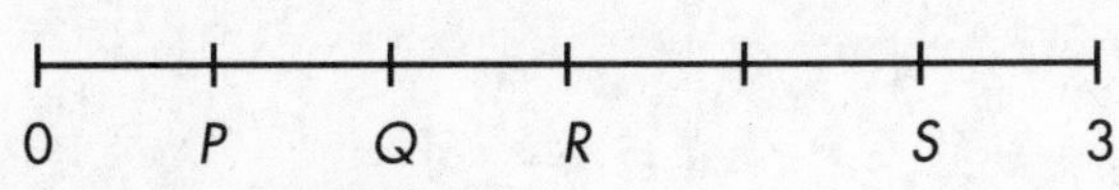


**A** Point *P*

**B** Point *Q*

**C** Point *R*

**D** Point *S*

**4.** A store gets a delivery of 347 boxes. The manager organizes all the boxes by putting 72 boxes in each of the store's warehouses and 59 boxes in the store's basement. How many warehouses does the store have?

______________________

**5.** A school band raises $615 to buy new drums. How many drums can the band buy for $84 each?

______________________

**6.** Subtract.

43.02 − 37.57

______________________

Name ______________________________



# 2-Digit Quotients

Find 866 ÷ 34.

**Step 1:** Round the divisor to the nearest ten. Look at the first digit in the divisor and the first digit in the dividend. What basic division fact is the best estimate of the quotient of these two numbers?

34)866 ⟶ 30)866

8 ÷ 3 = 2 R2

**Step 2:** Use this fact to begin the quotient. Write it over the tens place.

```
    2
34)866
  −68↓
   186
```

Multiply, 2 × 34 = 68.

Subtract and bring down the next digit in the dividend.

**Step 3:** What basic division fact is the best estimate of the next division? Use this fact and write it over the ones place.

```
   25 R16
34)866
  −68
   186
  −170
    16
```

Multiply, 5 × 34 = 170.

Subtract. Compare the remainder with the divisor. If the remainder is less than the divisor, write it in the quotient.

Check.

25 × 34 = 850

850 + 16 = 866

Complete.

**1.** 39)437   11 R ☐

**2.** 24)627   ☐☐ R3

**3.** 26)917   ☐☐ R☐

Divide. Check by multiplying.

**4.** 13)175

**5.** 44)508

**6.** April has 95 baseball cards. She wants to organize them on pages that hold 18 cards each. She has 5 pages. Does April have enough pages to organize all her cards?

______________________________

Name ______________________

Practice
**5-6**

# 2-Digit Quotients

In **1** through **6**, find each quotient.

**1.** $14\overline{)413}$ ________ **2.** $29\overline{)634}$ ________

**3.** $35\overline{)768}$ ________ **4.** $19\overline{)401}$ ________

**5.** $45\overline{)942}$ ________ **6.** $26\overline{)503}$ ________

**7.** The school student council sponsored a Switch Day where students were able to switch classes every 20 minutes. The students are in school for 7 hours. If a student switched as often as possible, how many classrooms in all did that student visit? (Hint: There are 60 minutes in 1 hour.)

______________________________________

**8.** 456 students participated in Switch Day. The students raised money for charity so that the principal would approve of the day. If the total amount of money raised was $912, and each student brought in the same amount of money, how much did each student raise?

______________________________________

**9.** The total dinner bill at a buffet came out to $589 for 31 people. About how much was the buffet cost per person?

**A** $15.00 **B** $20.00 **C** $22.00 **D** $25.00

**10.** If you have a two-digit divisor and a three-digit dividend, does the quotient always have the same number of digits?

______________________________________

______________________________________

Name ____________________

Enrichment
**5-6**

# Park Areas

The chart at the right shows the area, in square miles, of four parks. In the exercises below, write your answers in square miles.

| Park | Area (square miles) |
|---|---|
| A | 656 |
| B | 269 |
| C | 164 |
| D | 147 |

**1.** If you divided Park A into 32 equal parts, each containing a whole number of square miles, how large would each part be? How large would the remaining area be?

**2.** If you divided Park B into 53 equal parts, each containing a whole number of square miles, how large would each part be? How large would the remaining area be?

**3.** If you divided Park C into 16 equal parts, each containing a whole number of square miles, how large would each part be? How large would the remaining area be?

**4.** Complete the pictograph after choosing a picture to represent 32 $mi^2$. Be sure to represent any remaining area reasonably.

= 32 $mi^2$

| | |
|---|---|
| Park A | |
| Park B | |
| Park C | |
| Park D | |



 

Name ______________________________



**1.** Mr. Lee drives an average of 58 miles per hour. Which best describes how long he will take to drive 805 miles?

**A** Almost 52 hours

**B** Almost 51 hours

**C** Almost 14 hours

**D** Almost 13 hours

**2.** A school auditorium has 966 seats in 42 equal rows. How many seats are in each row?

**A** 23

**B** 24

**C** 42

**D** 43

**3.** A store clerk makes a display with 36 bags of beads. Each bag has 48 beads. How many beads are in the display?

**A** 1,728

**B** 1,488

**C** 432

**D** 372

**4.** Ms. Tanaka has $157 to spend on lunches this month. How many times this month can she buy a $13 lunch?

______________________________

**5.** The table shows the number of stars in four galaxies.

| Galaxy | Number of Stars |
|---|---|
| Galaxy J | 815,234,796,002 |
| Galaxy K | 851,243,679,010 |
| Galaxy L | 815,234,769,120 |
| Galaxy M | 851,432,697,201 |

List the galaxies in order from the least number of stars to the greatest number of stars.

______________________________

**6.** James runs on Monday and Tuesday. On Tuesday, he runs for 3 times as many minutes as he runs on Monday. What information do you need to find out the total time James runs on the two days?

______________________________

______________________________

______________________________



 

Name ____________________



# Estimating and Dividing with Greater Numbers

Find 8,037 ÷ 77.

You can use a calculator to divide large numbers.

**Step 1:** Estimate. Round the divisor and the dividend.
8,037 ÷ 77 ⟶
8,000 ÷ 80 = 100

The quotient should be close to 100.

**Step 2:** Now, use a calculator to find the quotient.
8,037 ÷ 77

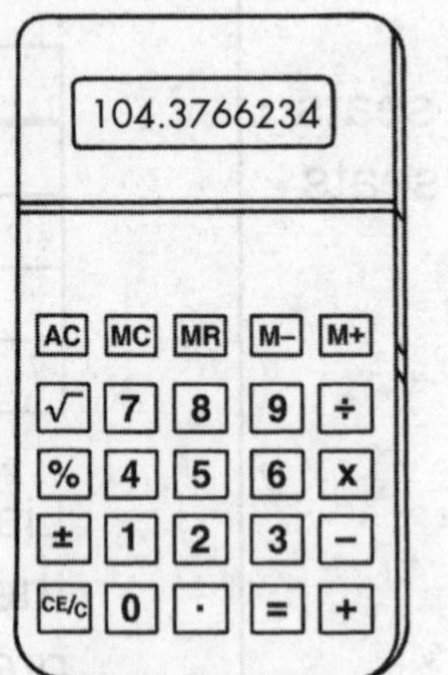


**Step 3:** Round the quotient to the required place. Remember, if the digit is 5 or more, add 1 to the rounding digit. If the digit is less than 5, leave the rounding digit alone.

Round the quotient to the nearest hundredth. 104.3766234 rounded to the nearest hundredth is 104.38. This is close to the original estimate, so the answer is reasonable.

Estimate first. Then use a calculator to find the quotient. Round to the nearest hundredth if necessary.

**1.** 78)3,796

**2.** 51)2,588

**3.** 38)3,914

**4.** 37)7,492

**5.** 46)6,725

**6.** 62)9,911

**7.** Is 5,309 ÷ 26 less than 20, greater than 20 but less than 200, or greater than 200?

____________________



 

Name ______________________________

Practice
**5-7**

# Estimating and Dividing with Greater Numbers

Estimate first. Then use a calculator to find the quotient. Round to the nearest hundredth if necessary.

**1.** $53\overline{)6{,}324}$ **2.** $52\overline{)6{,}348}$ **3.** $86\overline{)31{,}309}$ **4.** $33\overline{)3{,}455}$

**5.** 17,496 ÷ 91 = __________ **6.** 25,214 ÷ 47 = __________

**7.** 2,312 ÷ 26 = __________ **8.** 4,895 ÷ 83 = __________

The Humphrey family decided to fly from San Francisco to New York City, and from there to Rome, New Delhi, and finally Tokyo.

**9.** It took the Humphrey family 6 hours to travel from San Francisco to New York. How many kilometers did they travel per hour?

______________________________

| Distances by Plane | |
|---|---|
| San Francisco to New York | 4,140 km |
| New York to Rome | 6,907 km |
| Rome to New Delhi | 5,929 km |
| New Delhi to Tokyo | 5,857 km |

**10.** During the flight from New Delhi to Tokyo, flight attendants came through with snacks every 600 km. How many times did they come through?

______________________________

**11.** When the family arrived in New Delhi from Rome, the youngest son asked the pilot how fast he was flying the plane. The pilot told him about 847 km per hour. How many hours did it take the family to fly from Rome to New Delhi?

**A** 5 h **B** 6 h **C** 7 h **D** 8 h

**12.** Write a word problem that would require you to use 5,621 ÷ 23.

______________________________

Name ______________________________



# Teacher for a Day

You have been selected to be the teacher for a day. You are teaching division to your students. In the exercises below, explain how you can tell that each student has made an error. Then provide the correct quotient and remainder, if any.

1. Julie has written 4,411 ÷ 22 = 220.

______________________________

______________________________

2. Jorge has written 7,128 ÷ 36 = 202.

______________________________

______________________________

3. Jack has written 11,716 ÷ 58 = 212.

______________________________

______________________________

4. Jamie has written 2,244 ÷ 22 = 120.

______________________________

______________________________

Here are two divisibility rules to teach your students:

- A number is divisible by **8** if the last 3 digits are divisible by 8.
- A number is divisible by **9** if the sum of its digits is divisible by 9.

Are the following numbers divisible by 8 or 9, or both?

5. 202,008 __________ 6. 45,600 __________

7. 30,030,003 __________ 8. 2,160 __________

Name ______________________________

Daily Common Core Review

**5-8**

**1.** The table shows the amount of fish caught by three fishing boats.

**Fishing Totals**

| Boat | Pounds of Fish |
|---|---|
| *Mary B.* | 5,915 |
| *Sea Raider* | ? |
| *Clear Skies* | 3,276 |

The *Mary B.* caught about 12 times as much fish as the *Sea Raider.* About how many pounds of fish did the *Sea Raider* catch?

**A** About 500 pounds
**B** About 600 pounds
**C** About 5,000 pounds
**D** About 6,000 pounds

**2.** The *Clear Skies* sold the same amount of its fish to 28 seafood restaurants. If they sold all their fish, how many pounds did each restaurant buy?

**A** 128 pounds
**B** 117 pounds
**C** 110 pounds
**D** 101 pounds

**3.** How many more pounds of fish did the *Mary B.* catch than the *Clear Skies?*

**A** 1,629 pounds
**B** 1,729 pounds
**C** 2,639 pounds
**D** 2,761 pounds

**4.** A paper factory makes 8,423 sheets of paper in 45 minutes. How many sheets of paper does the factory make in 1 minute? Round to the nearest hundredth if necessary.

______________________________

**5.** Lila rolls a number cube two times. The first time she gets a 3. List all the possible outcomes of Lila's two rolls.

______________________________

______________________________

**6.** Nat has a rope that is 3.6 meters long. He cuts the rope into two pieces. One piece is 1.925 meters long. How long is the other piece of the rope?

______________________________

**7.** What is the value of the underlined digit below?

65,<u>2</u>08,193,977

______________________________

______________________________

Name ________________________________



# Problem Solving: Missing or Extra Information

Aiko bought 6 red balloons and 11 clear balloons for a party. During the party, 3 clear balloons burst but none of the red balloons did. How many clear balloons did Aiko have after the party?

**Read and Understand**

| | |
|---|---|
| What do you know? | Aiko bought 6 red balloons.<br>Aiko bought 11 clear balloons.<br>Three clear balloons burst during the party.<br>No red balloons burst during the party. |
| What are you trying to find? | The number of clear balloons remaining after the party |

**Plan and Solve**

Draw a picture of what you know.

| | |
|---|---|
| Solve the problem. | $11 - 3 = 8$ |
| Write the answer in a complete sentence. | Aiko had 8 clear balloons after the party. |

**Look Back and Check**

| | |
|---|---|
| Is your answer correct? | Yes, $8 + 3 = 11$ |

Look back at the items listed in "What you know."

1. What information helped you solve the problem?

_______________________________________________

2. What information did **NOT** help you solve the problem?

_______________________________________________

Name ______________________________

Practice
5-8

# Problem Solving: Missing or Extra Information

Decide if each problem has extra or missing information. Solve if possible.

1. It takes 4 hours to drive from Boston to New York. Jordan has a meeting in New York at 2:00 P.M. Can she arrive at her meeting on time?

______________________________

2. Franco hikes 4 miles each day for 5 days. He carries 100 ounces of water with him. It takes him 1 hour to hike 4 miles. How many hours did he hike in 5 days?

______________________________

3. Write a real-world problem that gives extra information. Under the problem write what the extra information is.

______________________________

4. Jorge buys T-shirts for $4 each and paints designs on them. He sells the designed T-shirts for $7 each. What information is needed to find how much profit he makes in one week?

   **A** The price of T-shirts at a store
   **B** The color of the T-shirts that he buys
   **C** The types of designs he draws on the T-shirts
   **D** The number of T-shirts he sells in one week

5. Krista can type 60 words per minute. She wrote an essay by hand in 5 hours, and it is now 4 pages long and has 500 words in it. She wants to type up her essay. About how long will it take to type her essay? Write what the extra or missing information is. Then solve if possible.

______________________________

______________________________

Name ______________________



# Information: Omitted or Spare?

Decide if each problem has extra or missing information. Solve if possible. Or provide possible information needed to solve the problem, and then solve it.

1. Karen is baking bread for her 5th-grade class. Each loaf can be cut into 8 slices. How many loaves should Karen bake if each student is served 2 slices?

2. Robert spelled 23 words correctly and 6 words incorrectly in his first spelling contest, 36 words correctly and 5 words incorrectly in his second spelling contest, and 29 words correctly and 4 words incorrectly in his third spelling contest. How many words did Robert spell correctly in all?

3. Carolina kayaked down the Hudson River for 4 days. She paddled 6 miles each morning and 9 miles each afternoon. The temperature ranged from 88° to 92° on her trip. How many total miles did Carolina paddle on her kayak trip?

Name ___________________________



**1.** Dr. Gallo's waiting room has a total of 18 magazines, including 3 fashion magazines. There are 5 more cooking magazines than there are decorating magazines. How many decorating magazines are there?

**A** 5
**B** 6
**C** 10
**D** 15

**2.** Gisela is putting her 35 CDs into categories. She has 11 that are pop music, and she has 3 times as many rock CDs as she has classical. How many rock CDs does Gisela have?

**A** 24
**B** 20
**C** 18
**D** 6

**3.** An order comes in to Extreme Skate Co. for 56 pairs of its most popular skate shoes, including 14 pairs of grey. The order calls for 4 times as many hot pink pairs as red pairs, and 3 more pairs of black than grey. How many pairs of hot pink shoes were ordered?

**A** 5
**B** 17
**C** 20
**D** 42

**4.** Arturo's Nursery has 48 tree seedlings ready to sell. There are 16 magnolia seedlings. There are 2 times as many dogwood seedlings as oak seedlings. There are 2 more magnolia seedlings than pine seedlings. How many of each type of seedling is ready to sell? Use the table.

| Seedling | Number Ready to Sell |
|---|---|
| Magnolia | 16 |
| Dogwood | |
| Oak | |
| Pine | |

**5.** Mr. Canela's 42 students voted on a class mascot. The gorilla received 8 votes. The python received 3 times as many votes as the giraffe, and the crocodile received 2 more votes than the gorilla. How many votes did each animal receive? Use the table.

| Mascot | Number of Votes |
|---|---|
| Gorilla | 8 |
| Python | |
| Giraffe | |
| Crocodile | |



 

Name ____________________



# Multiplying Decimals by 10, 100, or 1,000

You can use patterns to multiply decimals mentally by 10, 100, and 1,000.

Andrew starts selling his baseball cards for \$0.10 each. After selling 10 cards, he has made \$1.00. After selling 100 cards, he has made \$10.00.

\$.0.10

\$.0.10 × 10 = \$1.00

\$0.10 × 100 = \$10.00

When you multiply by

10 ($10^1$) Add 1 zero
100 ($10^2$) Add 2 zeros
1,000 ($10^3$) Add 3 zeros

If Andrew sold 1,000 cards, how much money would he make? ________

**Mental Math** For questions **1** through **4**, find the product using mental math.

**1.** 6.1 × 10 ________

**2.** 100 × 37.98 ________

**3.** 92.3 × 1,000 ________

**4.** 0.418 × 100 ________

**5.** Myla has an antique flower vase that she bought for \$15.75 many years ago. The vase's value is now 1,000 times as great. What is the value of the vase? ________

**6.** Raul can hit a golf ball 26.4 yards. A.J. can hit a golf ball 10 times as far. How far can A.J. hit the ball? ________

**7.** Is 0.018 a reasonable answer for 1.8 × 100?

________________________________________

________________________________________



 

Name ______________________

Practice 6-1

# Multiplying Decimals by 10, 100, or 1,000

Use mental math to find each product.

**1.** 53.7 × 10 ______

**2.** 74.3 × 100 ______

**3.** 66.37 × 1,000 ______

**4.** 1.03 × 10 ______

**5.** 92.5 × 10 ______

**6.** 0.8352 × 100 ______

**7.** 0.567 × 100 ______

**8.** 572.6 × 1,000 ______

**9.** 5.8 × 100 ______

**10.** 0.21 × 1,000 ______

**11.** 6.2 × 1,000 ______

**12.** 1.02 × 10 ______

**13.** 0.003 × 1,000 ______

**14.** 0.002 × 10 ______

**15.** 7.03 × 10 ______

**16.** 4.06 × 100 ______

**17.** Kendra bought 10 gallons of gasoline at $3.26 per gallon. How much did she pay for the gasoline?

**A** $326.00 **B** $32.60 **C** $1.26 **D** $0.26

**18.** Freddy is helping buy ingredients for salads for the school spaghetti dinner. He bought 10 pounds of onions at $0.69 per pound, 100 pounds of tomatoes at $0.99 pound, 1,000 pounds of bread crumbs at $0.09 per pound, and 100 pounds of lettuce at $0.69 per pound. Which of the items he bought cost the most?

**A** tomatoes **B** lettuce **C** bread crumbs **D** onions

**19.** Marco and Suzi each multiplied 0.721 × 100. Marco got 7.21 for his product. Suzi got 72.1 for her product. Which student multiplied correctly? How do you know?

______________________________

______________________________



 

Name ____________________

Enrichment
6-1

# Decimal Patterns

1. Jennifer sets her binoculars to enlarge objects 10 times their actual size. If the length of an ant is 0.52 inches, what is its length as seen through her binoculars?

_______________

2. A store has a contest to guess the weight of 1,000 black jellybeans on display in its window. If each of the jellybeans weighs 0.072 ounces, what is the total weight of all the jellybeans?

_______________

3. Jason saved $0.02 each day for 10,000 days. How much did he save in all?

_______________

4. Jefferson uses a microscope to observe a specimen in biology class. If his microscope enlarges objects 100 times their actual size and the specimen measures 0.009 inches, what is the size seen in the microscope?

_______________

5. Anya needs to buy 100 pounds of chocolate to make her holiday truffles. If chocolate sells for $0.49 per pound, how much will Anya spend?

_______________

6. Tim planted a tree that was 0.017 feet tall. After 10 years, the tree was 1,000 times as tall as when he planted it. What is the height of the tree after 10 years?

_______________

Name ____________________

Daily Common Core Review

**6-2**

**1.** Find the product.

6.5 × 5

**A** 33.5
**B** 32.5
**C** 32.0
**D** 30.5

**2.** Zoe plants a sunflower seed and tracks its growth. The seedling measures 3.71 inches after the first month. If Zoe's plant grows 3.71 inches each month for 12 months, how many inches tall will it be at the end of one year?

**A** 10.13 inches
**B** 34.52 inches
**C** 43.52 inches
**D** 44.52 inches

**3.** Find the sum.

68.47 + 121.35

**A** 52.88
**B** 63.98
**C** 189.72
**D** 189.82

**4.** Maria Elena is planning to paint a horizontal stripe around the middle of her bedroom. Each of her 4 walls measures 168.2 inches. How many inches long will the stripe be?

____________________

**5.** Find each product.

7.1 × 4 __________

0.33 × 9 __________

18.2 × 7 __________

0.078 × 2 __________

42.6 × 3 __________

23 × 0.05 __________

380 × 0.006 __________

6,400 × 0.2 __________



 

Name ______________________



# Estimating the Product of a Decimal and a Whole Number

You can estimate when you are multiplying a decimal by a whole number to check the reasonableness of your product.

Zane needs to buy 27 lb of roast beef for the company party. The roast beef costs $2.98 per pound. About how much will the roast beef cost?

There are two ways to estimate.

Round both numbers

$2.98 × 27

↓ ↓

$3 × 30 = $90

The roast beef will cost about $90.

Adjust your factors to compatible numbers you can multiply mentally.

$2.98 × 27

↓ ↓

$3 × 25 = $75

The roast beef will cost about $75.

Estimate each product.

**1.** 0.8 × 22 __________

**2.** 19.3 × 6 __________

**3.** 345 × 5.79 __________

**4.** 966 × 0.46 __________

Use the chart to answer questions **5** through **7**.

| Treatment | Cost |
|---|---|
| Shampoo | $7.95 |
| Haircut | $12.95 |
| Coloring | $18.25 |
| Perm | $22.45 |

**5.** About how much would it cost for Angelina and her 4 sisters to get a shampoo and a haircut?

**6.** Could 3 of the sisters get their hair colored for less than $100?

______________________________

**7.** Angelina gets 9 haircuts per year. About how much does she spend on haircuts for the year?

______________________________



 

Name ______________________________

Practice
**6-2**

# Estimating the Product of a Decimal and a Whole Number

Estimate each product using rounding or compatible numbers.

**1.** 0.97 × 312 ______

**2.** 8.02 × 70 ______

**3.** 31.04 × 300 ______

**4.** 0.56 × 48 ______

**5.** 0.33 × 104 ______

**6.** 0.83 × 12 ______

**7.** 0.89 × 51 ______

**8.** 4.05 × 11 ______

**9.** 0.13 × 7 ______

**10.** 45.1 × 5 ______

**11.** 99.3 × 92 ______

**12.** 47.2 × 93 ______

**13.** Mr. Webster works 4 days a week at his office and 1 day a week at home. The distance to Mr. Webster's office is 23.7 miles. He takes a different route home, which is 21.8 miles. When Mr. Webster works at home, he drives to the post office once a day, which is 2.3 miles from his house. Which piece of information is not important in figuring out how many miles Mr. Webster drives per week to his office?

**A** the number of days at the office
**B** the distance to his office
**C** the distance to the post office
**D** the distance from his office

**14.** Mrs. Smith bought her three children new snowsuits for winter. Each snowsuit cost $25.99. How much did Mrs. Smith pay in all?

**A** $259.90 **B** $77.97 **C** $51.98 **D** $25.99

**15.** How can estimating be helpful before finding an actual product?

______________________________

______________________________

______________________________



 

Name ______________________________

Enrichment

**6-2**

# Decimal Estimates

**1.** Georgia rollerskates 0.43 miles around her block each day. If she rollerskated 279 days in 2006, about how many miles did she rollerskate?

______________________________

**2.** Juan needs to buy 6.74 pounds of shrimp that sells for $9.68 per pound. Find an underestimate and an overestimate for the cost of the shrimp.

______________________________

**3.** Lana got a tip of 16%, or 0.16, for delivering pizza. If the pizza tab came to $38.19, about how much tip did she receive?

______________________________

**4.** Jerome needs to buy 26.9 yards of fabric to make bandannas for the Humane Society's dog parade. The fabric he chose costs $7.65 per yard. Find an underestimate and an overestimate for the cost of the fabric.

______________________________

**5.** Marcy picked 18.8 pounds of peaches at the pick-your-own orchard. Each pound of peaches costs $1.28. About how much will her peaches cost?

______________________________

**6.** Bruce jogs from his house to the library to tutor students and back again, a round trip of 0.56 miles. If Bruce tutored at the library 328 days in 2006, about how many miles did he jog?

______________________________

Name ______________________________

Daily Common Core Review

**6-3**

**1.** A company puts up a billboard every 4 miles along 432 miles of highway. How many billboards does the company put up?

**A** 10
**B** 18
**C** 108
**D** 180

**2.** During a sale, a grocery store gives every third customer a free loaf of bread. If the store gets 910 customers, how many loaves of bread does the store give away for free?

**A** 340
**B** 330
**C** 304
**D** 303

**3.** Which button has a letter with a pair of parallel lines?

**A** (K)
**B** (G)
**C** (R)
**D** (H)

**4.** A pet store can put no more than 5 fish in each tank. What is the least number of tanks the store needs to hold 354 fish?

______________________________

**5.** Write six billion, sixty-seven million, four hundred four thousand, thirteen in standard form.

______________________________

**6.** The Turner family saves $42 each month. How much have the Turners saved after 15 months?

______________________________


 

Name ____________________



# Number Sense: Decimal Multiplication

Amelia can walk 3.6 miles in one hour. How far will she walk in 2.1 hours?

**Step 1.** Estimate

$3.5 \times 2 = 7$

**Step 2.** Compare each factor to 1 to determine the relative size of the product.

$3.6 > 1$
$2.1 > 1$

Because both factors are greater than 1, your answer will be greater than both factors.

**Step 3.** Multiply as you would with whole numbers. Use reasoning to place the decimal appropriately.

$$\begin{array}{r} 3.6 \\ \times\ 2.1 \\ \hline 3\,6 \\ 7\,2\,0 \\ \hline 7.5\,6 \end{array}$$

↑

Amelia will walk 7.56 miles in 2.1 hours.

Solve. Check your answer for reasonableness.

1. $\begin{array}{r} 1.6 \\ \times\ 0.3 \\ \hline \end{array}$

2. $\begin{array}{r} 0.8 \\ \times\ 0.2 \\ \hline \end{array}$

3. $\begin{array}{r} 12.8 \\ \times\ 3.2 \\ \hline \end{array}$

4. $\begin{array}{r} 0.03 \\ \times\ 6 \\ \hline \end{array}$

5. Explain why $0.3 \times 0.9 \neq 2.7$. What is the correct answer?

________________________________________

________________________________________

6. **Mental Math** Estimate the product of 3.9 and 4.6 using mental math. Explain the method you used.

________________________________________

________________________________________



 

Name ______________________________

Practice
**6-3**

# Number Sense: Decimal Multiplication

For 1-8 only two numbers of the product are shown. Also, the decimal point is missing. Complete the product and place the decimal point where it should be. Round your answer to the nearest hundredth.

**1.** $0.4 \times 0.6 =$ 2 4

**2.** $3.6 \times 4.1 =$ 1 4

**3.** $9.01 \times 8.3 =$ 7 4

**4.** $4.06 \times 20.1 =$ 8 1.

**5.** $0.2 \times 0.8 =$ 1 6

**6.** $4.04 \times 3 =$ 1 2

**7.** $11.6 \times 3.4 =$ 3 9

**8.** $7.8 \times 0.1 =$ 7 8

For 9-12 complete the operation and explain why you placed the decimal point where you did.

**9.** $1.8 \times 0.3 =$ ______________________________

______________________________

**10.** $0.2 \times 0.7 =$ ______________________________

______________________________

**11.** $12.4 \times 3.1 =$ ______________________________

______________________________

**12.** $9.5 \times 3 =$ ______________________________

______________________________



 

Name ____________________



# Family Fun

Ron has 4 more sisters than he has brothers, and he has 2 brothers. He is one-third the age of his eldest brother. He is three times the age of his youngest sister. For the exercises below, tell if the statement about Ron's family is true or false and explain why.

**1.** If Ron's brothers are represented by the variable $b$, and his sisters are represented by the variable $s$, $b \times 4 = s$ represents the number of sisters he has.

____________________

____________________

**2.** If the age of Ron's youngest sister is represented by the variable $y$, and Ron's age is represented as $r$, his youngest sister's age can be represented as $\frac{y}{r} = 3$.

____________________

**3.** If the age of Ron's oldest brother is represented by the variable $x$ and Ron's age is represented as $r$, Ron's age can be represented as $\frac{x}{3} = r$.

____________________

**4.** If the number of sisters Ron has is represented by the variable $s$, then the number of brothers he has can be represented as $s + 4$.

____________________

____________________

**5.** There are 8 children in Ron's family.

____________________

____________________

____________________



 

Name ______________________________

Daily Common Core Review

**6-4**

**1.** At the Bright-O Shampoo factory, 6.35 ounces of chemicals are added to water. Of the chemicals, 1.078 ounces are vanilla oil. Which amount of the chemicals is **NOT** vanilla oil?

**A** 0.05272 ounces

**B** 0.5272 ounces

**C** 5.272 ounces

**D** 52.72 ounces

**2.** Which of the following is equivalent to $8 \times 8 \times 8 \times 8 \times 8$?

**A** $8 \times 5$

**B** $8^5$

**C** $5^8$

**D** 4,096

**3.** It is projected that the population of the United States in 2050 will be 419,854,000. Write that number in expanded notation using exponents.

______________________________

______________________________

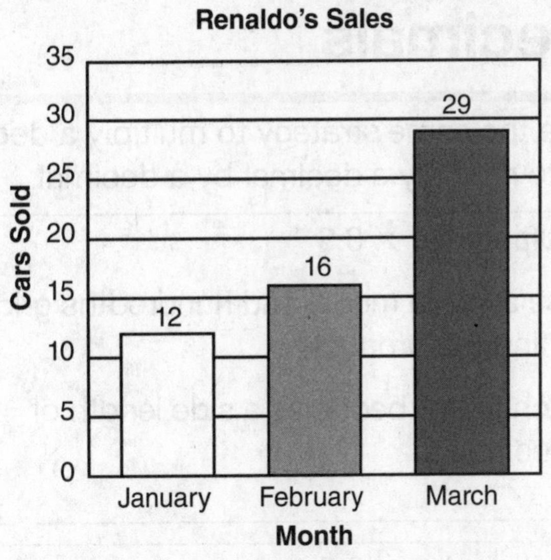


**4.** Renaldo owns a used car lot. What is the total number of cars Renaldo sold during the three months?

______________________________

**5.** Renaldo makes $956.75 for each car that he sells. Estimate how much money he made during the three months.

______________________________



 

Name ______________________

Reteaching
**6-4**

# Models for Multiplying Decimals

Use the same strategy to multiply a decimal by a whole number or to multiply a decimal by a decimal.

Multiply 1.0 × 0.3

Use an area model and hundredths grid to find the product.

Each factor becomes a side length of a rectangle.

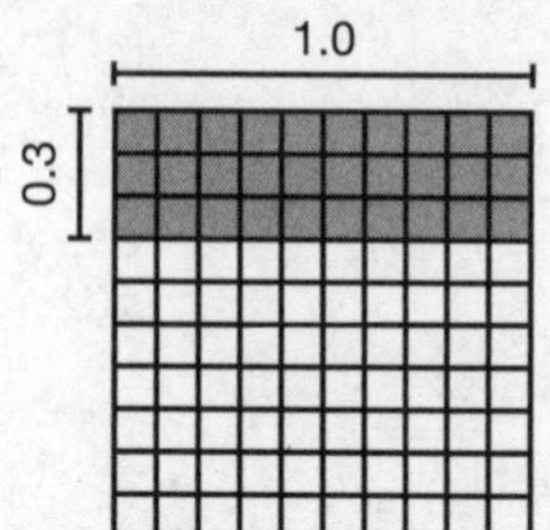


Count the hundredths cells in the shaded area to find the product.

1.0 × 0.3 = 0.3

Multiply 1.6 × 0.6

Use an area model and a hundredths grid to find the product.

Because one factor is greater than 1, you will need to use 2 hundredths grids (for a total of 2 units).

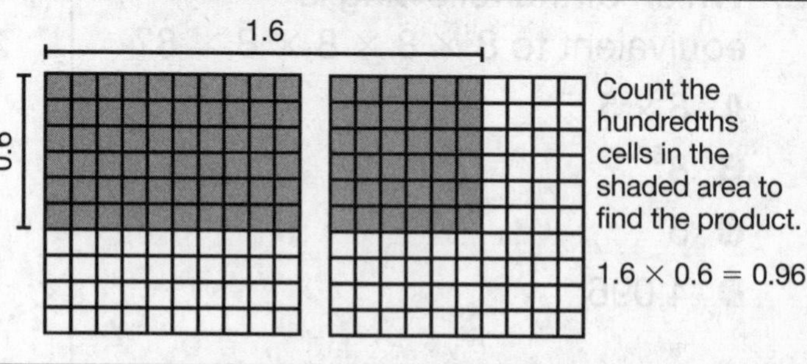


Count the hundredths cells in the shaded area to find the product.

1.6 × 0.6 = 0.96

Place the decimal point in each product.

**1.** 1.2 × 3.6 = 432 ____________ **2.** 5.5 × 3.7 = 2035 ____________ **3.** 4.4 × 2.3 = 1012 ____________

Find the product.

**4.** 7 × 0.5 ________ **5.** 12 × 0.08 ________ **6.** 24 × 0.17 ________

**7.** 0.4 × 0.7 ________ **8.** 1.9 × 0.4 ________ **9.** 3.42 × 5 ________

**10.** If you multiply two decimals less than 1, can you predict whether the product will be less than or greater than either of the factors? Explain.

______________________________________________

______________________________________________



 

Name ______________________

Practice
**6-4**

# Models for Multiplying Decimals

Place the decimal point in each product.

**1.** $3 \times 6.89 = 2067$ ______ **2.** $0.3 \times 4.5 = 1350$ ______

Find each product.

**3.** $14.3 \times 2.1 \times 8 =$ ______ **4.** $0.45 \times 100 =$ ______

**5.** $67.1 \times 0.3 \times 40 =$ ______ **6.** $58 \times 4.21 =$ ______

**7.** Show how to find the product of $16.2 \times 4$ using addition.

______________________

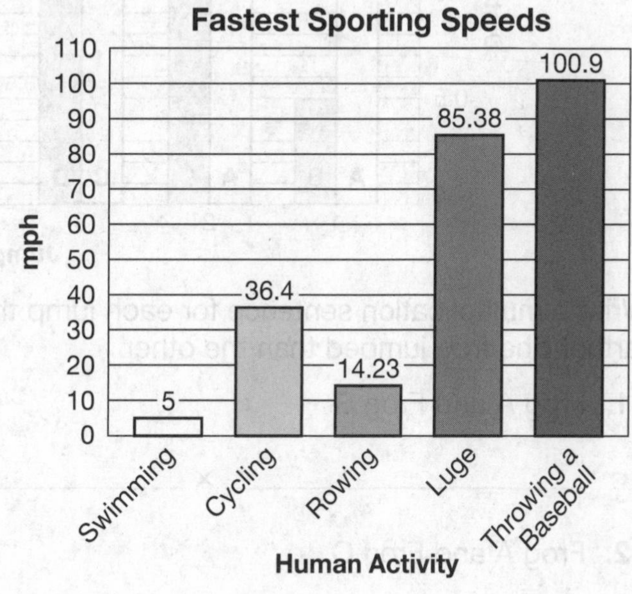


**8.** Which activity is 6 times faster than the fastest rowing speed?

______________________

**9.** The fastest speed a table tennis ball has been hit is 21.12 times faster than the speed for the fastest swimmer. What is the speed for the table tennis ball?

______________________

**10.** How fast would 3 times the fastest rowing speed be?

______________________

**11.** Which is the product of $241.82 \times 3.1$?

**A** 7.498 **B** 749.642 **C** 74.958 **D** 7.5

**12.** Explain why multiplying $37.4 \times 0.1$ gives a product that is less than 37.4.

______________________

______________________

______________________

Name ______________________



# Frog Jumpers

Midvale Middle School held its annual carnival. The frog-jumping contest is a popular attraction at the carnival. The graph below shows how far the frogs jumped.

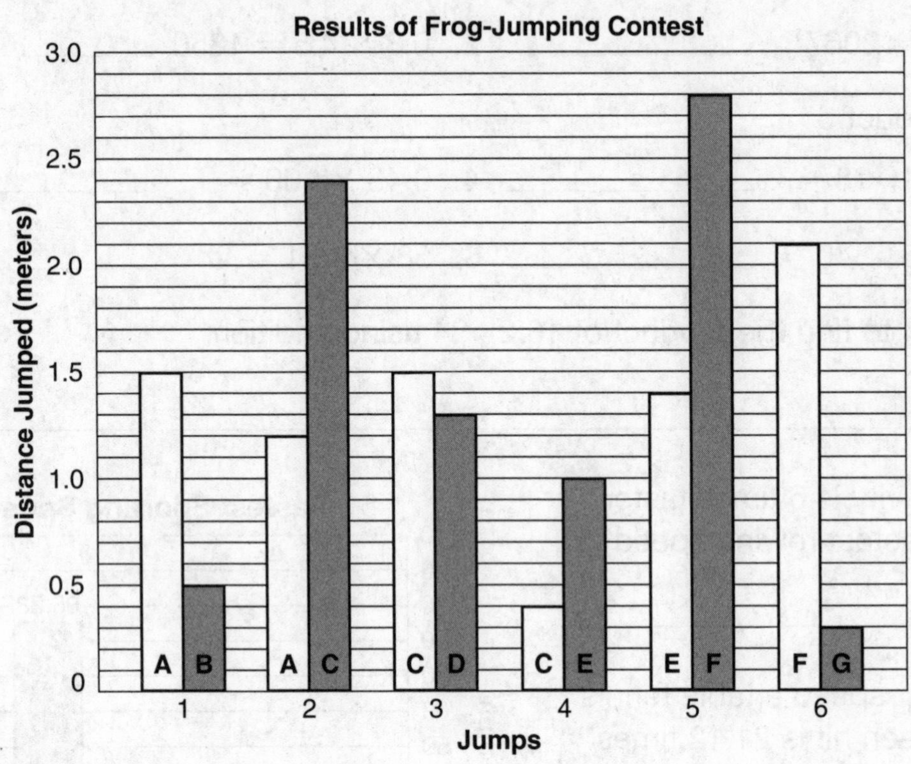


Write a multiplication sentence for each jump that shows how much farther one frog jumped than the other.

**1.** Frog A and Frog B

______ × ______ = ______

**2.** Frog A and Frog C

______ × ______ = ______

**3.** Frog C and Frog E

______ × ______ = ______

**4.** Frog E and Frog F

______ × ______ = ______

**5.** Frog F and Frog G

______ × ______ = ______



 

Name ______________________________

Daily Common Core Review

**6-5**

**1.** Find the product.

$9.3 \times 100$

**A** 0.093
**B** 93
**C** 930
**D** 9,300

**2.** Saul earns $25.75 each time he takes care of the Norman family's pets over a long weekend. If he takes care of the Normans' pets for 10 long weekends this year, how much money will he have earned?

**A** $2,575.00
**B** $257.50
**C** $35.75
**D** $2.575

**3.** Find the difference.

$54.59 - 26.61$

**A** 81.20
**B** 38.98
**C** 32.18
**D** 27.98

**4.** Kelvin rides the bus 7.78 miles to school each day. After 100 days of riding the bus, how many miles has he spent on the bus on the way to school?

______________________________

______________________________

**5.** Use mental math to find each product.

$0.07 \times 10$ ________

$4.41 \times 100$ ________

$0.05 \times 1{,}000$ ________

$12.77 \times 100$ ________

$0.26 \times 1{,}000$ ________

$0.03 \times 10$ ________



 

Name ______________________



# Multiplying a Decimal by a Whole Number

Travis can read a book chapter in 2.6 hours. The book has 18 chapters. How long will it take Travis to read the book?

Step 1. Use powers of 10 to multiply as you would with whole numbers.

$2.6 \times 10^1 = 26$
$18 \times 1 = 18$

$$\begin{array}{r} 26 \\ \times\ 18 \\ \hline 208 \\ +\ 260 \\ \hline 468 \end{array}$$

Step 2. Divide the whole number answer by $10^1$ so that the number of decimal places in the factors and the product does not change.

$468 \div 10^1 = 46.8$

Step 3. Use reasoning to check your answer. Since 2.6 is greater than one, the answer should be greater than 18. Because 46.8 is greater than 18, your answer is reasonable.

It will take Travis 46.8 hours to read the book.

For questions **1** through **3**, find the product.

**1.** $\begin{array}{r} 2.3 \\ \times\ \ 6 \\ \hline \end{array}$

**2.** $\begin{array}{r} 71.7 \\ \times\ \ 12 \\ \hline \end{array}$

**3.** $\begin{array}{r} 0.89 \\ \times\ \ 21 \\ \hline \end{array}$

**4.** Sara is making pillows. Each pillow requires 1.7 yards of fabric. How many yards of fabric will Sara need to make 9 pillows?

______________________

**5.** Light bulbs usually cost \$2. They are on sale for 0.50 of the regular price. What is the sale price? Is this a better price than if the sale price were 0.35 of the regular price?

______________________

______________________

Name ______________________

Practice
6-5

# Multiplying a Decimal by a Whole Number

Find each product.

**1.** $5.4 \times 3$

**2.** $3.8 \times 4$

**3.** $0.55 \times 8$

**4.** $8.19 \times 5$

Insert a decimal point in each answer to make the equation true.

**5.** $5 \times 6.3 = 315$ ______________

**6.** $3.01 \times 9 = 2709$ ______________

Use the table at the right for Exercises **7–9.**

**7.** Which desert accumulates the least amount of rain in August?

______________

**Average Desert Rainfall in August**

| Desert | Average Rainfall |
|---|---|
| Reno | 0.19 mm |
| Sahara | 0.17 mm |
| Mojave | 0.1 mm |
| Tempe | 0.24 mm |

**8.** If each month in Reno had the same average rainfall as in August, what would the total number of millimeters be after 12 months?

______________

**9.** In December, the average total rainfall in all of the deserts together is 0.89 mm. Explain how to use the figures from the table to write a comparison of the total desert rainfall in August and December.

______________

______________

______________

**10.** If $4n = 3.60$, which is the value of $n$?

**A** 0.09 **B** 0.9 **C** 9 **D** 90



 

Name ______________________

Enrichment
**6-5**

# How Much Faster?

Ryan's Deli makes a sandwich in 1 min. The chart at the right indicates how long it takes other delis to make a sandwich in comparison to Ryan's. For example, Werner's Deli takes 2.2 times as long to make a sandwich as Ryan's. For the exercises below, determine if the statement is reasonable or unreasonable. Explain your answer.

| Deli | Time Factor |
|---|---|
| Werner's | 2.2 |
| Main Street | 0.6 |
| Two Star | 3.74 |

**1.** In 10 min, Ryan's Deli will make more than twice as many sandwiches as Werner's Deli.

______________________

______________________

______________________

**2.** In 30 min, Main Street Deli will make more than twice as many sandwiches as Ryan's Deli.

______________________

______________________

______________________

**3.** It takes the Two Star Deli under 38 min to make 10 sandwiches.

______________________

______________________

______________________

______________________


 

Name ______________________________



**1.** Ms. MacDowell is buying her class of 27 students end-of-year gifts. Each gift costs $3.39, including tax. About how much is Ms. MacDowell spending on gifts for her students? Use the rounding strategy.

**A** about $60
**B** about $80
**C** about $90
**D** about $120

**2.** Estimate the product using compatible numbers.

$0.67 \times 623$

**A** about 420
**B** about 280
**C** about 42
**D** about 36

**3.** Find the difference: $73.92 - 49.63$.

**A** 34.39
**B** 34.29
**C** 24.39
**D** 24.29

**4.** Estimate each product using rounding or compatible numbers.

$0.67 \times 322$ __________

$3.12 \times 71$ __________

$18.88 \times 23$ __________

$207 \times 0.51$ __________

$0.16 \times 44$ __________

$0.42 \times 25$ __________

$1.91 \times 787$ __________

**5.** For math class, Boone is using his shoe to measure one of his classroom walls. He finds that the wall is 27 shoes long. His shoe measures 9.8 inches long. Use compatible numbers to find about how many inches long the wall is.

______________________________



 

Name ___________________________

Reteaching

**6-6**

# Multiplying Two Decimals

Caroline earns \$2.40 per hour for babysitting her brother. She babysat last night for 3.25 hours. How much did she earn?

First, estimate your product so you can check for reasonableness.

$\$2.40 \times 3.25$

$\downarrow \quad \downarrow$

$\$2 \times 3 = 6$ Caroline earned about \$6.00.

**Step 1:** Multiply each factor by powers of 10 to create whole numbers. Then multiply these numbers.

$2.40 \times 10^2 = 240$
$3.25 \times 10^2 = 325$

$$\begin{array}{r} 325 \\ \times\ \ 240 \\ \hline 000 \\ 13{,}000 \\ +65{,}000 \\ \hline 78{,}000 \end{array}$$

**Step 2:** Because you multipled each factor by $10^2$, you must divide your answer by $10^2$ two times.

$78{,}000 \div 10^4 = 7.8000$

$7.8000 = \$7.80$

Caroline earned \$7.80 last night. Because \$7.80 is close to your estimate of \$6, your answer is reasonable.

Find each product. Check by estimating.

**1.** $0.2 \times 4.6$ ________ **2.** $3.9 \times 7.1$ ________ **3.** $8.54 \times 0.1$ ________

**4.** $0.53 \times 6.4$ ________ **5.** $9.3 \times 5.86$ ________ **6.** $0.37 \times 4.4$ ________

**7.** Jackie wants to buy a new CD player. It costs \$32.95. She has saved \$26 and has a coupon for 30% off the price. Does Jackie have enough money to buy the CD player?

_______________________________________________

_______________________________________________

_______________________________________________



 

Name ______________________

Practice
6-6

# Multiplying Two Decimals

Find each product.

**1.** 3.2 × 0.3

**2.** 4.4 × 0.2

**3.** 8.6 × 3.4

**4.** 1.9 × 0.05

**5.** 0.79 × 4.3 = ________

**6.** 0.8 × 0.05 = ________

**7.** The product of 4.7 and 6.5 equals 30.55. What is the product of 4.7 and 0.65? 4.7 and 65?

______________________

**8.** What would be the gravity in relation to Earth of a planet with 3.4 times the gravity of Mercury?

______________________

**Relative (to Earth) Surface Gravity**

| Planet | Gravity |
|---|---|
| Mercury | 0.39 |
| Neptune | 1.22 |
| Jupiter | 2.6 |

**9.** The gravity of Venus is 0.35 times that of Jupiter. What is the gravity of Venus in relation to Earth's gravity?

______________________

**10.** How many decimal places are in the product of a number with decimal places to the hundredths multiplied by a number with decimal places to the tenths?

**A** 2 **B** 3 **C** 4 **D** 5

**11.** Explain how you know the number of decimal places that should be in the product when you multiply two decimal numbers together.

______________________

______________________

______________________

______________________



 

Name ______________________________

Enrichment
**6-6**

# Decimal Dinners

**1.** Gina wants to bake pumpkin pies for a Thanksgiving potluck dinner. She needs 8.8 pounds of pumpkins that sell for $0.93 per pound. How much will she spend? Round to the nearest cent.

______________________________

**2.** Tony is making his sweet-potato side dish for the potluck. Sweet potatoes are on sale at the market for $0.67 per pound. If Tony needs 9.3 pounds of sweet potatoes, how much will he spend? Round the cost to the nearest cent.

______________________________

**3.** Reba is making a tablecloth for the dessert table. She needs to decide between the autumn-leaf fabric that sells for $4.99 per yard and the turkey-print fabric that sells for $5.75 per yard. If Reba needs 3.6 yards, how much will she spend for each of the fabrics? Round the cost to the nearest cent.

______________________________

**4.** Jack is mixing hot apple-cider punch for the potluck. His recipe calls for 12.4 quarts of apple cider. If apple cider sells for $1.82 per quart, how much will Jack spend? Round the cost to the nearest cent.

______________________________

**5.** Lindsay is in charge of buying turkeys for Thanksgiving dinner. The turkeys she has selected weigh a total of 49.5 pounds. If turkey is on sale for $2.17 per pound, how much will Lindsay spend? Round the cost to the nearest cent.

______________________________

**6.** Wayne is making a string-bean casserole for the potluck. He needs 3.8 pounds of string beans, which sell for $0.82 per pound. How much will Wayne spend on string beans? Round the cost to the nearest cent.

______________________________

Name ______________________________

Daily Common Core Review
**6-7**

**1.** An apartment complex has 91 apartments. There are 177 cars in the complex parking lot. Which is the best estimate of the number of cars per apartment?

**A** About 1
**B** About 2
**C** About 10
**D** About 20

**2.** A town is 28 square miles in area. The town's population is 2,603. Which is the best estimate of the number of people per square mile?

**A** About 9
**B** About 13
**C** About 90
**D** About 130

**3.** Frank earns $7 per hour. How much does Frank earn for working 19 hours?

**A** $133
**B** $106
**C** $73
**D** $26

**4.** A copy shop prints 5,493 pages. They use the pages to make 68 same-size booklets. About how many pages are in each booklet?

______________________________

______________________________

**5.** Twenty-three students make paper flowers to decorate their classroom. Each student makes 12 flowers. How many flowers did the students make altogether?

______________________________



 

Name ______________________

Reteaching
**6-7**

# Problem Solving: Multiple-Step Problems

Faye is putting together packets of colored beads to give as gifts. The chart shows the beads she had on hand yesterday. This morning she bought 4 boxes of yellow beads containing 45 beads each. How many packets of 60 beads can she put together?

| Trinket Beads | |
|---|---|
| **Color** | **Number** |
| Red | 195 |
| Blue | 170 |
| Green | 175 |

Find the hidden question or questions.

**1.** How many yellow beads are there? **1.** $45 \times 4 = 180$

**2.** How many beads are there in all? **2.** $195 + 170 + 175 + 180 = 720$

Solve. $720 \div 60 = 12$

Write the answer in a sentence. Faye will make 12 packets.

**Look Back and Check**

Is the answer reasonable? Yes. Since $60 \times 10 = 600$, the answer is reasonable.

**1.** Faye decides to double the number of yellow beads in the mix. How many packets will she make if she fills each packet with 60 beads? ______

**2. Explain It** Suppose Faye plans to fill packets with 60 beads after deciding not to add any yellow beads to the mix. If you want to find how many packets she can put together, what hidden question or questions would you have to ask? Explain.

______________________________

______________________________

Name ______________________

Practice
6-7

# Problem Solving: Multiple-Step Problems

Write and answer the hidden question. Then solve.

**1.** Gloria talked on her cell phone for 320 minutes the first month, 243 minutes the second month, and 489 minutes the third month. Her payment package does not allow her to pay per minute; she can only buy packages. If she has to pay $25 for every 200 minutes, how much did she pay for the first three months?

______________________

______________________

______________________

______________________

**2.** Each can of paint will cover 450 tiles. Augustin is painting 300 tiles in his bathroom, 675 in his kitchen, and 100 in his hallway. How many cans of paint does he need to buy?

______________________

______________________

**3.** The sum of three different numbers is 18. If every number is a prime number, what are the three numbers?

______________________

______________________

**4.** You earn $3 an hour as a waitress. After working 3 hours, you earn $12, $5, and $7 in tips. How much money did you earn in total? Explain how you found your answer.

______________________

______________________



 

Name ______________________________

Enrichment **6-7**

# Hearty Roots

An organic farm opened a farm stand to sell vegetables. Help the customers spend their money wisely.

**Hearty Roots**

| Vegetable | Price |
|---|---|
| Cucumbers | $0.50 each or $3.75 for a bag of 10 |
| Tomatoes | $1.98 for 1 lb or $3.55 for 2 lb |
| Zucchini | $0.60 each or $5.59 for a dozen |

**1.** One customer bought three 2-lb bags of tomatoes. How much did he save by buying these instead of six 1-lb bags?

______________________________

**2.** Another customer bought 8 cucumbers, 10 zucchini, and 1 pound of tomatoes. Based on the money he spent, show how the customer could have purchased more vegetables for less money.

______________________________

______________________________

______________________________

______________________________

______________________________

**3.** You have $20.00 to spend at Hearty Roots. Give an example of how you could get the best value for the money. Tell what you would buy and how much money you would have left over.

______________________________

______________________________

______________________________

______________________________

Name ______________________

Daily Common Core Review

**7-1**

**1.** A computer can load 1,247 megabytes in 40 seconds. Which best describes the loading speed of the computer?

**A** Around 20 megabytes per second

**B** Nearly 28 megabytes per second

**C** Close to 31 megabytes per second

**D** More than 40 megabytes per second

**2.** The table shows the number of square feet painted by three house painters.

| Painter | Square Feet Painted | Days Worked |
|---|---|---|
| Megan | 604 | 5 |
| John | 521 | 4 |
| Cathy | 460 | 3 |

Which best describes John's average painting speed?

**A** About 120 square feet per day

**B** About 130 square feet per day

**C** About 140 square feet per day

**D** About 150 square feet per day

**3.** A model of 1-foot cubes is shown below.

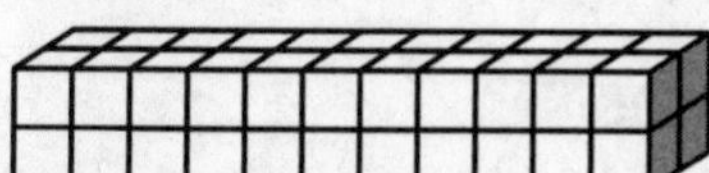

What is the volume of this model?

**A** 50 cubic feet

**B** 44 cubic feet

**C** 40 cubic feet

**D** 34 cubic feet

**4.** List the painters in Question 2 in order from slowest to fastest average painting speed.

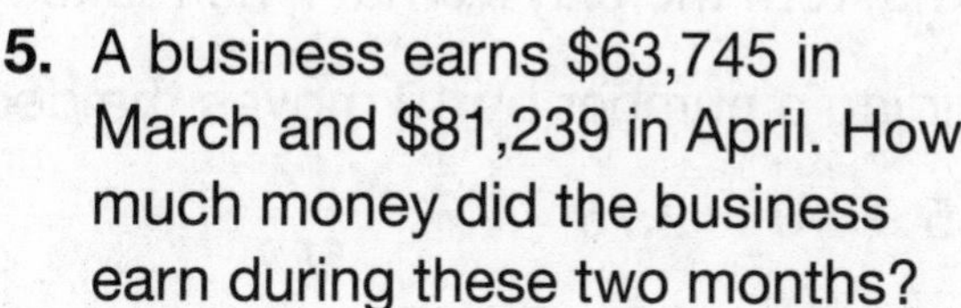

______________________

______________________

**5.** A business earns $63,745 in March and $81,239 in April. How much money did the business earn during these two months?

______________________

**6.** The graph shows the number of votes for each person in a school election.

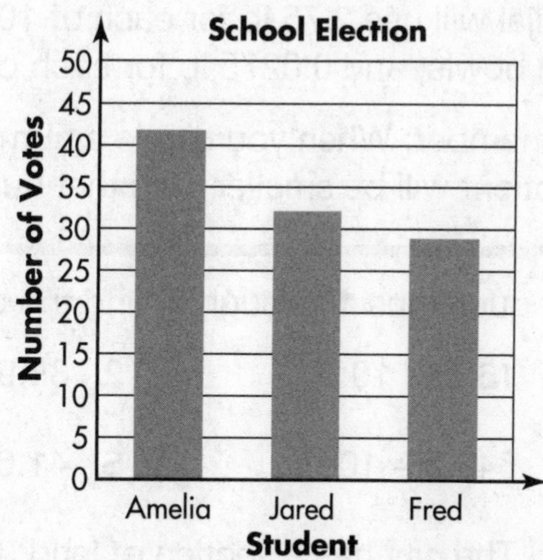


Which student won the election?

______________________



 

Name ____________________



# Dividing Decimals by 10, 100, or 1,000

You can use place-value patterns when you divide a decimal by 10, 100, or 1,000.

Sanjai has 27.5 lb of clay. If he uses the clay to make 10 bowls, how much clay will he use for each bowl? What if he makes 100 bowls from the clay? What if he makes 1,000 bowls?

Dividing a number by 10 moves the decimal point one place to the left.

$27.5 \div 10 = 2.75$

Dividing a number by 100 moves the decimal point two places to the left.

$27.5 \div 100 = 0.275$

Dividing a number by 1,000 moves the decimal point three places to the left.

$27.5 \div 1{,}000 = 0.0275$

Sanjai will use 2.75 lb for each of 10 bowls, 0.275 lb for each of 100 bowls, and 0.0275 lb for each of 1,000 bowls.

Remember: When you divide a number by 10, 100, or 1,000, your quotient will be smaller than that number.

For questions **1** through **6**, find the quotient. Use mental math.

**1.** $16.4 \div 10$ **2.** $38.92 \div 100$ **3.** $297.1 \div 100$

**4.** $540.9 \div 10$ **5.** $41.628 \div 1{,}000$ **6.** $0.33 \div 10$

**7.** The city has a section of land 3,694.7 ft long. The city wants to make 100 equal-sized gardens with this land. How long will each garden be?

____________________

**8.** Connor divided 143.89 by 100. He said his answer was 14.389. Is this a reasonable answer?

____________________

____________________

____________________

Name ___________________________

Practice
**7-1**

# Dividing Decimals by 10, 100, or 1,000

Find each quotient. Use mental math.

**1.** 86.6 ÷ 10 = __________ **2.** 192.5 ÷ 100 = __________

**3.** 1.99 ÷ 100 = __________ **4.** 0.87 ÷ 10 = __________

**5.** 228.55 ÷ 1,000 = __________ **6.** 0.834 ÷ 100 = __________

**7.** 943.35 ÷ 1,000 = __________ **8.** 1.25 ÷ 10 = __________

Write 10, 100, or 1,000 for each *n*.

**9.** 78.34 ÷ *n* = 0.7834 **10.** 0.32 ÷ *n* = 0.032 **11.** (75.34 − 25.34) ÷ *n* = 5

__________ __________ __________

**12.** There are 145 children taking swimming lessons at the pool. If 10 children will be assigned to each instructor, how many instructors need to be hired? __________

**13.** Ronald ran 534.3 mi in 100 days. If he ran an equal distance each day, how many miles did he run per day?

**A** 5 **B** 5.13 **C** 5.343 **D** 6.201

**14.** Carlos says that 17.43 ÷ 100 is the same as 174.3 × 0.01. Is he correct? Explain.

_______________________________________________

_______________________________________________



 

Name ______________________________



# Dividing Decimals

Find each quotient. Use mental math.

**1.** 783.9 ÷ 10 ____________

**2.** 35.6 ÷ 100 ____________

**3.** 591.72 ÷ 1,000 ____________

**4.** 54.8 ÷ 10 ____________

**5.** 2.17 ÷ 100 ____________

**6.** 92.5 ÷ 1,000 ____________

**7.** 6.36 ÷ 10 ____________

**8.** 475.1 ÷ 100 ____________

**9.** 81.3 ÷ 1,000 ____________

**10.** 0.076 ÷ 10 ____________

**11.** 793 ÷ 100 ____________

**12.** 8,324 ÷ 1,000 ____________



 

Name ______________________________



Use mental math to find each quotient.

**1.** 33.23 ÷ 1,000

**A** 0.003323

**B** 0.03323

**C** 0.3323

**D** 3.323

**2.** 0.02 ÷ 100

**A** 0.2

**B** 0.02

**C** 0.002

**D** 0.0002

**3.** Estimate 3,982 ÷ 38.

**A** 1

**B** 10

**C** 100

**D** 1,000

**4.** What is the first step in finding 492 ÷ 50?

______________________________

______________________________

______________________________

**5.** Suppose there are 1,200 pencils in 30 jars with an equal number of pencils per jar. Write an expression to show how to find the number of pencils per jar.

______________________________

______________________________

______________________________

______________________________



 

Name ______________________



# Estimating Decimal Quotients

When estimating with decimal division, you can use compatible numbers to make the math easier. By rounding the dividend and the divisor to numbers that can easily be divided, you will make your math computation easier.

Estimate 88.95 ÷ 0.95.

88.95 ÷ 0.95 = ? Write the original problem.

↓ ↓

90 ÷ 0.90 = 100 Write compatible numbers.

For questions 1-4, estimate the quotients.

**1.** 12.72 ÷ 3.6 ______________

**2.** 9.39 ÷ 0.92 ______________

**3.** 0.74 ÷ .08 ______________

**4.** 145.22 ÷ 50.2 ______________

**5.** Mario and three friends purchased a snow blower to share. If the snow blower costs $439.20, describe how you estimate how much each person will pay?

______________________________

______________________________

______________________________

______________________________

______________________________

**6.** Is 100 a reasonable estimate for 915.25 ÷ 88.22?

______________________________

______________________________

______________________________



 

Name ________________________

Practice **7-2**

# Estimating Decimal Quotients

Use compatible numbers to find each quotient.

**1.** 2.90 ÷ 29 ____________ **2.** 0.65 ÷ 5.1 ____________

**3.** 48 ÷ 3.2 ____________ **4.** 18.2 ÷ 11 ____________

**5.** 0.18 ÷ 0.33 ____________ **6.** 55 ÷ 10.7 ____________

**7.** 152 ÷ 5.12 ____________ **8.** 117.8 ÷ 0.12 ____________

**9.** 41.9 ÷ 19 ____________ **10.** 0.6 ÷ 5 ____________

**11.** 33.90 ÷ 10.2 ____________ **12.** 145 ÷ 0.3 ____________

**13.** 502 ÷ 9.5 ____________ **14.** 435.2 ÷ 39 ____________

**15.** 180.8 ÷ 6 ____________ **16.** 60 ÷ 5.9 ____________

**17.** 48 ÷ 3.33 ____________ **18.** 1.8 ÷ 20 ____________

**19.** Martin is saving for a gaming system. The total cost of the gaming system and three games is $325.49. About how much money should he save per week to purchase the gaming system and games in 10 weeks?

**A** About $0.33

**B** About $3.30

**C** About $33.00

**D** About $330.00

**20.** Kayla works as a hairdresser. She earned $248.50 in tips in five days. If she earned the same amount each day, about how much did Kayla earn per day? Explain your answer.

______________________________________________

______________________________________________

______________________________________________



 

Name ______________________



# Currency Conversion

## Get the Most for Your Money!

Different currencies are used around the world. The Yen is the currency used in Japan. This table shows the currency exchange rates for the Yen on the first business day of October of each year.

| Date | Yen (¥) Exchange Rate per U.S. Dollar ($) |
|---|---|
| October 2, 2000 | 108.81 |
| October 1, 2001 | 120.27 |
| October 1, 2002 | 122.73 |
| October 1, 2003 | 110.61 |
| October 1, 2004 | 110.45 |
| October 3, 2005 | 114.17 |
| October 2, 2006 | 117.66 |
| October 1, 2007 | 115.91 |
| October 1, 2008 | 106.06 |
| October 1, 2009 | 89.73 |
| October 1, 2010 | 83.30 |

Source: U.S. Federal Reserve

Use compatible numbers to write a number sentence and to estimate the value of money in U.S. Dollars for each value.

1. 55 ¥ in 2003 ______________________
2. 200 ¥ in 2002 ______________________
3. 270 ¥ in 2009 ______________________
4. 725 ¥ in 2001 ______________________
5. 325 ¥ in 2004 ______________________
6. 250 ¥ in 2006 ______________________
7. 880 ¥ in 2007 ______________________
8. Which is a better value for your money, 800 ¥ in 2000 or 800 ¥ in 2010. Explain your answer using estimation.

______________________



 

Name ______________________________

Daily Common Core Review

**7-3**

**1.** Mrs. Sheffield's class library has many different kinds of books. She has a total of 122 books, including 57 books about science. There are 23 more books about different countries than there are books about sports. How many sports books are there? You can use cubes to act out the problem.

**A** 65 sports books

**B** 42 sports books

**C** 34 sports books

**D** 21 sports books

**2.** Which of these numbers falls between 4.598 and 4.603?

**A** 4.597

**B** 4.599

**C** 4.604

**D** 4.7

**3.** Molly bought 4.23 meters of pink ribbon and 8.56 meters of orange ribbon to make costumes for a play. How much material did she buy in all?

**A** 3.33 meters

**B** 4.33 meters

**C** 12.79 meters

**D** 13.79 meters

**4.** Estimate the product $16.1 \times 42.98$. Show your work.

______________________________

______________________________

______________________________

**5.** For science class, Sammy is using the length of his stride to measure the length of the field outside his school. He finds that the field is 157 strides long. His stride measures 1.4 meters long. Use compatible numbers to find about how many meters long the field is.

______________________________

______________________________

______________________________

______________________________



 

Name ______________________

Reteaching

**7-3**

# Number Sense: Decimal Division

You have learned how to estimate when dividing with decimals. You can also use number sense to place the decimal point in the quotient.

How many quarters are in $3.50?

When you divide decimals by decimals, you can just divide the decimals as if they are whole numbers. After finding the quotient, place the decimal by estimation.

$3.50 ÷ 0.25 = ? Write the original problem

350 ÷ 25 = 14 Whole-number division

Place the decimal: 14. Use estimation

How many quarters are in $3.50? __________

For questions **1-4**, place the decimal correctly.

**1.** 9.72 ÷ 3.6 = 2 7 __________

**2.** 6.39 ÷ 0.72 = 8 8 7 5 __________

**3.** 0.81 ÷ 0.09 = 9 0 __________

**4.** 1.08 ÷ 0.27 = 4 0 __________

**5.** Nathan and Jorge are working on a decimal division problem in math class. After finishing the problem, it looked like this: 4.76 ÷ 2.5 = 0.19. Nathan said that the decimal is incorrectly placed in the quotient, and Jorge disagrees. Who is right? Explain your answer.

______________________________

______________________________

______________________________

**6.** Is 1.72 a reasonable answer for 86.25 ÷ 0.5?

______________________________

______________________________



 

Name ______________________

Practice **7-3**

# Number Sense: Decimal Division

Use estimation to place each decimal point.

**1.** 7.84 ÷ 0.28 = 2 8 0 ________

**2.** 0.65 ÷ 0.13 = 0 5 0 ________

**3.** 0.144 ÷ 1.2 = 1 2 0 ________

**4.** 9.61 ÷ 31 = 0 3 1 ________

**5.** 25.2 ÷ 0.42 = 0 6 0 ________

**6.** 8.4 ÷ 0.2 = 4 2 ________

**7.** 14.74 ÷ 2.2 = 6 7 0 ________

**8.** 28.9 ÷ 0.17 = 1 7 0 ________

**9.** 48.4 ÷ 0.22 = 2 2 0 ________

**10.** 7.6 ÷ 3.3 = 2 3 0 ________

**11.** 101.6 ÷ 6.8 = 1 4 9 4 ________

**12.** 0.148 ÷ 0.2 = 0 7 4 ________

**13.** 9.6 ÷ 0.12 = 0 8 0 ________

**14.** 75.15 ÷ 15.12 = 4 9 7 ________

**15.** 9.824 ÷ 3.2 = 3 0 7 ________

**16.** 0.93 ÷ 31 = 0 0 3 0 ________

**17.** 22.785 ÷ 14.7 = 1 5 5 ________

**18.** 11.56 ÷ 0.34 = 0 3 4 0 ________

**19.** Mr. Harrison bought 42 kilograms of salt for his science classes. Each group needs 0.75 kilogram of salt for their experiment. How many groups does Mr. Harrison have in his science classes?

**A** 0.56 **B** 5.6 **C** 56 **D** 560

**20.** Roman and Ranjan each divided 3.56 by 0.72. Roman got 4.94 for his quotient. Ranjan got 0.04 for his quotient. Which student divided correctly? How do you know?

______________________________________________

______________________________________________

______________________________________________

Name ______________________________



# Number Sense

**Place the Decimal!**

1. Santonio bought a box of cookies for $3.84. If there are 24 cookies in the box, how much did Santonio pay per cookie? ______________________

2. The 34 students in Mrs. Roblin's dance class are buying her a special pin for the dance show. If the pin costs $326.74, how much will each student pay? ______________________

3. Molly opened a savings account to save for a bicycle. She deposited the same amount of money each week. At the end of 18 weeks, she had saved $331.56. How much money did Molly deposit into her account each week? ______________

4. The 5 children in the Chu family bought their father a watch for a present. If the watch costs $174.95 and each child put forth an equal amount, how much did each spend on the watch? ______________________

5. Doughnuts cost $3.45 for a dozen at Store A, and cost $2.40 for 8 at Store B. Which store has a cheaper cost per doughnut? ______________________

______________________________________________

6. A little league baseball team went out for pizza to celebrate their victory. The total on the bill at the pizza place was $87.60. If all 12 players shared the bill equally, how much did each of the players pay? ______________________

7. Braedyn is buying a microscope for $228.72. She is paying in 12 weekly installments. How much will Braedyn pay each week? ______________________



 

Name ______________________________

Daily Common Core Review

**7-4**

**1.** Brad used the compatible numbers 510 ÷ 20 for an estimate. Which quotient might he be finding?

**A** 5380 ÷ 59

**B** 522 ÷ 21

**C** 277 ÷ 31

**D** 84 ÷ 9

Use this table for Exercises **2** through **3.**

**Summer Sale**

| | Regular Price | Sale Price |
|---|---|---|
| Sunglasses | $15.79 | $12.95 |
| Flip-Flops | $ 8.78 | $ 4.89 |
| Swimsuits | $46.50 | $24.59 |

**2.** At the sale, Jessica bought 4 pairs of sunglasses. How much did she spend?

**A** $51.58

**B** $51.80

**C** $55.80

**D** $54.80

**3.** Leah bought 2 pairs of flip-flops and a swimsuit. How much money did she save by buying them on sale?

**A** $29.75

**B** $29.69

**C** $29.48

**D** $36.80

**4.** Draw a line perpendicular to this line.

**5.** How can you check that this answer is correct?
24,230 ÷ 0.5 = 48,460

______________________________

Name ______________________

Reteaching
**7-4**

# Dividing by a Whole Number

Find 196 ÷ 32.

**Step 1**

Put the decimal point in the dividend. Divide. Put the decimal in the quotient right above the decimal in the dividend. Subtract.

```
      6.
32 ) 196.
    -192
       4
```

**Step 2**

Add a zero after the decimal point in the dividend. Bring down the zero. Divide. Subtract.

```
      6.1
32 ) 196.0
    -192
       4 0
      -3 2
         8
```

**Step 3**

Repeat Step 2 until there is no remainder.

```
      6.125
32 ) 196.000
    -192
       4 0
      -3 2
         80
        -64
         160
        -160
           0
```

Remember, you can use estimation to see if your answer is reasonable: 180 ÷ 30 = 6. You can check your answer using multiplication: 32 × 6.125 = 196

Find the quotient.

**1.** 11)93.5 ______

**2.** 25)1.75 ______

**3.** 6)573 ______

**4.**
```
     6.
3 ) 18.6
   -18
     0
```
______

**5.**
```
     3.
7 ) 22.61
   -21
```
______

**6.**
```
      $ 3.
12 ) $44.40
     - 36
        8
```
______

**7.** Cherri said that 0.9 ÷ 3 = 0.3. Is she correct? Explain why or why not.

______________________

______________________

______________________

Name ____________________

Practice

7-4

# Dividing by a Whole Number

Find the quotient.

**1.** $42.78 ÷ 3 ______ **2.** 66.5 ÷ 5 ______ **3.** 8.4 ÷ 10 ______

**4.** 5 ÷ 500 ______ **5.** 59.6 ÷ 4 ______ **6.** 188.4 ÷ 30 ______

**7.** $1.25 ÷ 5 ______ **8.** 235 ÷ 40 ______ **9.** 11.8 ÷ 25 ______

**10.** Jorge bought 6 tickets to a concert for $324. What was the cost of each ticket?

______

**11.** Tony bought a 72-ounce box of dog biscuits. How many pounds of dog biscuits did he buy? (Remember: 1 pound = 16 ounces.)

**A** 4 pounds

**B** 4.5 pounds

**C** 90 pounds

**D** 4,320 pounds

**12.** Janell uses 66 beads for each necklace she makes. She bought a bag of 500 beads. How many necklaces can she make?

______

**13.** In what place is the first digit of the quotient for 18.88 ÷ 4? Tell how you know.

______

______

Name ____________________

Enrichment
**7-4**

# Fruit Market

Howard went grocery shopping and bought different amounts of fruit. The table shows partial data for the kinds, prices, and amounts of fruit Howard bought. Complete the table and then answer the questions.

| | Fruit | Number of Pounds | Price per Pound | Total Price |
|---|---|---|---|---|
| **1.** | Strawberries | 4 | | $11.56 |
| **2.** | Cherries | 6 | | $15.54 |
| **3.** | Bananas | 12 | | $10.68 |
| **4.** | Raspberries | 5 | | $20.05 |

**5.** How does the price per pound of raspberries compare to the price per pound of strawberries?

______________________________

______________________________

______________________________

**6.** How does the price per pound of cherries compare to the price per pound of bananas?

______________________________

______________________________

______________________________

**7.** Howard is using the fruit to make a salad for a party. His friend said he would pay half the cost of the fruit. How much will each person pay?

______________________________

**8.** How much does each pound of fruit salad cost to make?

______________________________

**9.** If each pound of fruit salad feeds two people, how many people will Michael's fruit salad feed?

______________________________



 

Name ______________________________



**1.** James earns a commission on every used car he sells. Last month, James had a sales total of \$97,686.50. What was the average price for the 4 cars he sold last month?

**A** \$26,408.40
**B** \$24,421.63
**C** \$264.08
**D** \$26.41

**2.** At the zoo, detailed records are kept for each animal. This chart shows the weight of a tiger cub. During which period was the weight gain the lowest?

| Month | Weight (lbs) |
|---|---|
| April | 12.63 |
| May | 15.81 |
| June | 18.06 |
| July | 22.47 |
| August | 25.9 |
| September | 28.58 |

**A** June to July
**B** May to June
**C** August to September
**D** July to August

**3.** Joe started in Albany, NY, and drove to Baltimore, MD (525 km), and then on to Nashville, TN (1133 km), and on to Phoenix, AZ (2,716 km), and finally on to Portland, OR (2168 km). Estimate the total length of his trip.

______________________________

______________________________

**4.** Estimate the quotient: $420.4 \div 28.6$.

______________________________

**5.** Estimate the product: $75.2 \times 9.7$.

______________________________

Name ____________________



# Dividing a Whole Number by a Decimal

To divide a whole number by a decimal, multiply both numbers by a power of 10 to make the divisor a whole number.

**Divide:** 138 ÷ 0.04

Multiply by 100 to make 0.04 a whole number. Remember to multiply 138 by 100, too.

$0.04 \times 100 = 4$ $\quad\quad$ $138 \times 100 = 13{,}800$

Use long division to find the quotient:

```
   3,450
4)13,800
  12
   1 8
   1 6
     20
     20
```

So, 138 ÷ 0.04 = 3,450.

Use long division to find each quotient.

**1.** 0.3)780 ________ **2.** 0.5)406 ________ **3.** 0.02)1140 ________

**4.** 0.06)282 ________ **5.** 0.08)312 ________ **6.** 0.04)619 ________

Find each quotient.

**7.** 154 ÷ 0.7 ________ **8.** 3510 ÷ 0.9 ________ **9.** 228 ÷ 0.3 ________

**10.** 467 ÷ 0.02 ________ **11.** 106 ÷ 0.05 ________ **12.** 581 ÷ 0.04 ________

**13.** 3900 ÷ 0.08 ________ **14.** 207 ÷ 0.03 ________ **15.** 721 ÷ 0.25 ________

**16.** A kitchen floor has an area of 48 square feet. One tile covers 0.75 square foot. How many tiles would be needed to cover the entire kitchen floor? ________

**17.** Mark says that to divide 58 by 0.65, you only need to multiply both numbers by 10 because that will give you a whole number. Jan says you need to multiply both numbers by 100. Who is correct and why?

____________________

____________________



 

Name ______________________



# Dividing a Whole Number by a Decimal

**Find each quotient. Show your work.**

**1.** $0.7\overline{)840}$ ________ **2.** $0.3\overline{)1,230}$ ________ **3.** $0.05\overline{)281}$ ________

**4.** $0.7\overline{)287}$ ________ **5.** $0.6\overline{)135}$ ________ **6.** $0.08\overline{)280}$ ________

**7.** 4,530 ÷ 0.06 ________ **8.** 315 ÷ 0.9 ________ **9.** 516 ÷ 0.03 ________

**10.** 827 ÷ 0.2 ________ **11.** 45 ÷ 0.15 ________ **12.** 1,233 ÷ 0.09 ________

**13.** A 21-pound turkey was cooked for a small banquet. The caterer figures he will discard 5 pounds of bones and that each person will eat 0.8 pounds of the remaining turkey. How many people will the turkey serve?

______________________

**14.** During a regular half-hour TV show, there are 8 minutes of commercials. If each commercial is 0.25 minutes long, how many commercials will be shown during that show?

______________________

**15.** A machine in a deli cooks chickens by rotating them past a heat source. One rotation takes 1.75 minutes, and it takes 35 minutes to fully cook a chicken. How many rotations does it take to cook the chicken?

**A** 8 **B** 14 **C** 18 **D** 20

**16.** One pound of horsehair is divided into "pulls" to make horsehair belts. One "pull" weighs about 0.011 ounces. How many "pulls" could be made from 6 pounds of horsehair?

______________________

**17.** When you divide a whole number by a decimal less than 1, the quotient is greater than the whole number. Why?

______________________

______________________



 

Name ______________________

Enrichment
**7-5**

# Class of 2008

Circle the letter that describes the best answer choice.

**1.** Mr. Davis teaches fifth grade. In September there were 12 girls and 13 boys in his class. In October one of the girls moved away. In January two boys joined the class. How many boys are there in Mr. Davis's class now?

**A** There are more boys than girls in the class.

**B** There are more boys now than there were in September.

**C** There are 15 boys in Mr. Davis's class now.

**2.** In the entire fifth grade, there are 41 girls and 46 boys. About $\frac{3}{4}$ of the students are right-handed. Are there more than or less than 60 students who are right-handed?

**A** Between 62 and 63 students are right-handed.

**B** More than 60 students are right-handed.

**C** About $\frac{1}{4}$ of the students are left-handed.

**3.** About $\frac{5}{6}$ of the students in the fifth-grade accelerated math program go on to earn a college degree. There are currently 26 fifth graders in the accelerated math program. How many students will probably earn a college degree?

**A** About twenty fifth graders will probably earn a college degree.

**B** Less than 26 fifth graders will probably earn a college degree.

**C** About 10 fifth graders will not earn a college degree.

**4.** The table shows the number of boys and girls in the fifth grade for four years. How many more boys than girls were in the fifth grade in 2004?

**Fifth Graders**

| Year | Boys | Girls |
|---|---|---|
| 2004 | 44 | 38 |
| 2005 | 43 | 48 |
| 2006 | 42 | 56 |
| 2007 | 46 | 51 |

**A** There were more boys than girls in the fifth grade in 2004.

**B** There were 6 more boys than girls in the fifth grade in 2004.

**C** There were more girls than boys in 2007.

Name ____________________

Daily Common Core Review
**7-6**

**1.** Matt attends exercise classes 5 times each week. Estimate how many classes he will attend in one year.

**A** About 50

**B** About 150

**C** About 200

**D** About 250

**2.** Estimate what fraction of the figure is not shaded.

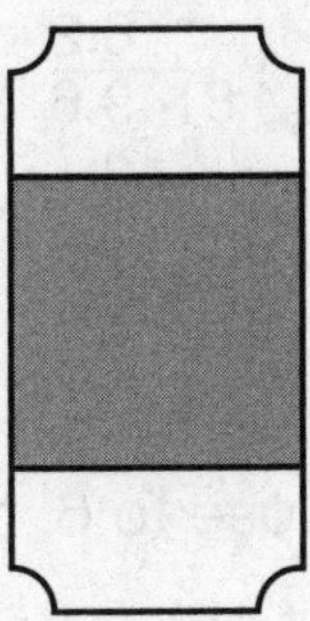

____________________

Use >, <, or = to compare each pair of numbers.

**3.** 12.562 ◯ 12.625

**4.** 9.62 ◯ 9.26

**5.** 125.62 ◯ 126.25

**6.** 0.962 ◯ 0.926

**7.** Find the quotient.
4500 ÷ 1.2 = ____________

Name ______________________________

Reteaching
**7-6**

# Dividing a Decimal by a Decimal

When you divide by a decimal, you need to rewrite the dividend and the divisor so that you are dividing by a whole number.

Find 4.96 ÷ 0.8.

**Step 1:** Estimate. Use compatible numbers.

480 ÷ 80 = 6

**Step 2:** Make the divisor a whole number. Multiply the divisor AND the dividend by the same power of 10.

Place the decimal point in the quotient.

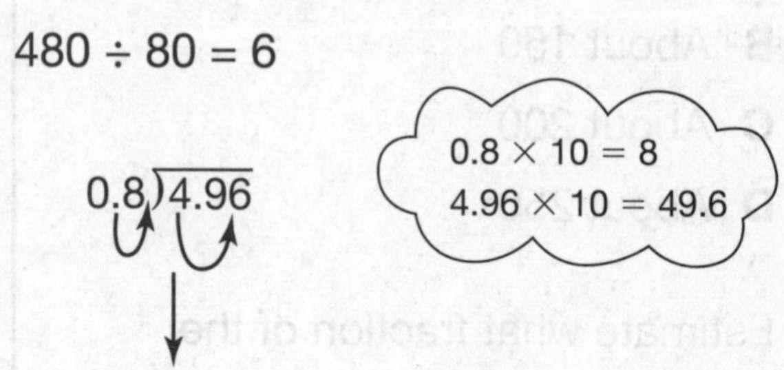


**Step 3:** Divide as you would with whole numbers. Remember that sometimes you may need to annex zeros to complete your division.

8)49.6 → 8)49.6 = 6.2
48
16
16
0

**Step 4:** Compare the quotient with your estimate.

Because 6.2 is close to 6, the answer checks.

Find each quotient.

**1.** 0.02)1.5

Estimate: ______________________

Multiply dividend and divisor by what power of 10? ________

Place the decimal point in the quotient.

Divide. How many zeros do you need to annex? ________

Compare the quotient to your estimate.
Is the answer reasonable? ______________

**2.** 0.06)0.36 **3.** 0.04)9.6 **4.** 0.75)0.03

**5.** Fernando used tenths grids to draw this picture showing 1.6 ÷ 0.4 = 4. Draw a picture to show 1.8 ÷ 0.6. Write the quotient.

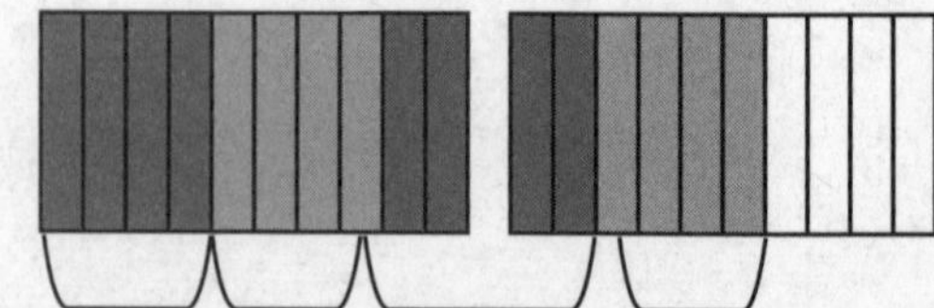



 

Name ______________________

Practice
**7-6**

# Dividing a Decimal by a Decimal

Find each quotient.

**1.** $8.4 \div 0.03 =$ ______

**2.** $66.15 \div 0.063 =$ ______

**3.** $100.5 \div 1.5 =$ ______

**4.** $860 \div 0.04 =$ ______

**5.** $72.8 \div 10.4 =$ ______

**6.** $14.36 \div 0.04 =$ ______

**7.** $2.87 \div 0.1 =$ ______

**8.** $78.2 \div 0.2 =$ ______

**9.** How does multiplying both the dividend and the divisor by a factor of 10 sometimes make a problem easier to solve?

______

______

For each item, find how many times greater the 2011 cost is than the 1955 cost. Round your answer to the nearest hundredth.

| Item | 1955 Cost | 2011 Cost |
|---|---|---|
| Movie admission | $0.75 | $9.50 |
| Regular popcorn | $0.25 | $4.25 |
| Regular drink | $0.35 | $2.75 |

**10.** movie admission ______

**11.** regular popcorn ______

**12.** regular drink ______

**13.** Which item has increased the greatest amount of times from its original cost? ______

**14.** Divide. Round to the nearest hundredth. $250.6 \div 1.6$

**A** 156 **B** 156.6 **C** 156.61 **D** 156.63

**15.** Allison and Rhea got different quotients when they divided 4.80 by 0.12. Whose work is correct? Explain why.

Allison: $12\overline{)4.80}$ = 0.40

Rhea: $12\overline{)480}$ = 40.0

______

______

Name ______________________________



# Pyramid Division

Use the digits on the pyramids to form the divisor and dividend for each quotient.

**1.**

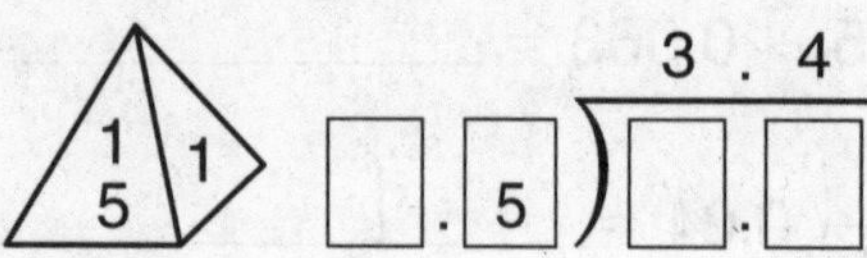


**2.** (Pyramid: 9, 3, 3) $\square.2\overline{)\square.\square 3 6}$ = 1.230

**3.**

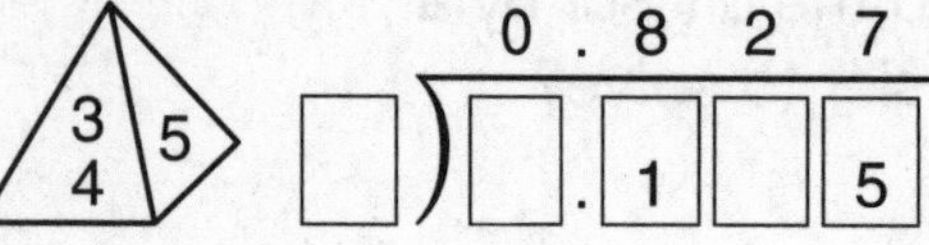


**4.** (Pyramid: 8, 3, 4, 6) $1.\square\overline{)\square.7\square\square}$ = 2.365

**5.** (Pyramid: 1, 2, 6) $\square\square.6 \div \square = 3.6$

**6.** (Pyramid: 6, 2, 7) $\square\square 9.\square \div 3.\square = 22$

**7.** (Pyramid: 0, 3, 6) $\square.\square \div 7.\square = 0.9$

**8.** (Pyramid: 1, 5, 4, 8) $\square.\square 1\square \div \square.4 = 3.87$

Name ______________________________



1. Find the quotient.
2.7 ÷ 0.9

**A** 30
**B** 3
**C** 0.3
**D** 0.03

2. Benjamin finished his triathlon in 12.44 hours. During the race, he drank 460.28 fluid ounces of liquid. How many fluid ounces did he drink per hour?

**A** 3.7 fl oz
**B** 3.788 fl oz
**C** 37 fl oz
**D** 37.88 fl oz

3. Which answer is correct?
347.14 − 58.71

**A** 311.63
**B** 299.43
**C** 298.43
**D** 288.43

For **4** and **5,** use the chart below.

| Candy | Price per Piece |
|---|---|
| Gumballs | $0.08 |
| Sour Straws | $0.04 |
| Jawbreakers | $0.40 |
| Licorice Rope | $0.16 |

4. Tania brings $8.32 to the candy store. She wants to buy 21 jawbreakers. Does she have enough money? Round your answer down to the nearest whole number.

______________________________

______________________________

______________________________

______________________________

______________________________

5. Tania divides her money into two equal amounts. How many sour straws can she buy with half of her money? How many licorice ropes can she buy with the second half of her money?

______________________________

______________________________



 

Name ______________________________

Reteaching
**7-7**

# Problem Solving: Multiple-Step Problems

A multiple-step problem is a problem where you may need more than one step to find your answer.

Marcie was in a 3-day charity walk. Her friend Gayle said she would give the charity \$1.50 for each mile that Marcie walked. The first day, Marcie walked 26.42 miles. The second day, Marcie walked 32.37 miles. The third day, Marcie walked 28.93 miles. How much money did Gayle give?

**Step 1.** Read through the problem again and write a list of what you already know.

*Marcie walked 26.42, 32.37, and 28.93 miles.*
*Gayle gave \$1.50 for each mile.*

**Step 2.** Write a list of what you *need* to know.

*Total amount Gayle gave*

**Step 3.** Write a list of the steps to solve the problem.

*Find the total number of miles Marcie walked.*
*Find the amount Gayle gave.*

**Step 4.** Solve the problem one step at a time.

$26.42 + 32.37 + 28.93 = 87.72$ *total number of miles Marcie walked*

$87.72 \times \$1.50 = \$131.58$ *total amount Gayle gave*

Use the information above to answer Exercise **1**.

**1.** Marcie's brother Tom was also in the charity walk. He only walked 0.8 as far as Marcie on the first day, 0.7 as far on the second day, and 0.9 as far on the third day. How many miles did Tom walk, rounded to the nearest hundredth of a mile?

______________________________

**2.** Diego is buying fruit at the store. Which costs less: 1 pound of each fruit or 4 pounds of peaches?

| **Fruit** | **Cost per pound** |
|---|---|
| Apples | \$0.89 |
| Oranges | \$1.29 |
| Peaches | \$0.99 |
| Grapes | \$1.09 |

______________________________

Name ______________________________



# Problem Solving: Multiple-Step Problems

Write and answer the hidden question or questions in each problem and then solve the problem. Write your answer in a complete sentence.

| Storewide Sale | |
|---|---|
| Jeans | $29.95 for 1 pair<br>OR 2 pairs for $55.00 |
| T-shirts | $9.95 for 1<br>OR 3 T-shirts for $25.00 |

1. Sue bought 2 pairs of jeans and a belt that cost $6.95. The tax on the items was $5.85. Sue paid the cashier $70.00. How much money did Sue receive in change?

______________________________

2. A recreation department purchased 12 T-shirts for day camp. The department does not have to pay sales tax. It paid with a $100.00 bill. How much change did it receive?

______________________________

______________________________

3. When Mrs. Johnson saw the sale, she decided to get clothes for each child in her family. She bought each of her 6 children a pair of jeans and a T-shirt. She paid $14.35 in sales tax. How much was Mrs. Johnson's total bill?

**A** $94.35 **B** $119.70 **C** $229.35 **D** $253.35

4. Write a two-step problem that contains a hidden question about buying something at the mall. Tell what the hidden question is and solve your problem. Use $8.95 somewhere in your equation. Write your answer in a complete sentence.

______________________________

5. What are hidden questions and why are they important when solving multiple-step problems?

______________________________

______________________________



 

Name ____________________



# Smart Shoppers

Mr. Murphy owns a fruit stand in the city. People buy fruit all day long as they pass by. Help the customers spend their money wisely.

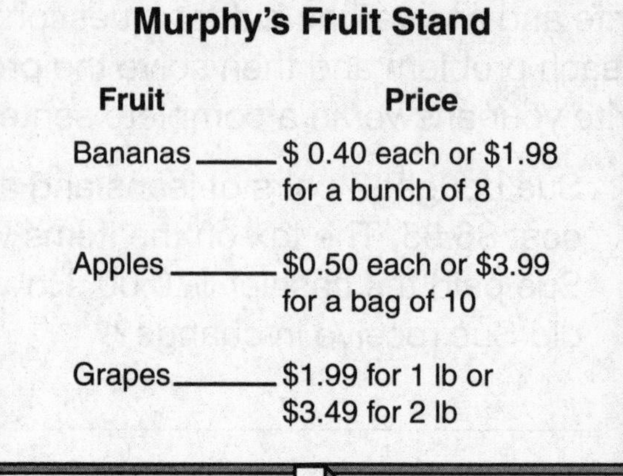

**Murphy's Fruit Stand**

| Fruit | Price |
|---|---|
| Bananas | $ 0.40 each or $1.98 for a bunch of 8 |
| Apples | $0.50 each or $3.99 for a bag of 10 |
| Grapes | $1.99 for 1 lb or $3.49 for 2 lb |

**1.** One customer bought two 2-lb bunches of grapes. How much did she save by buying these instead of four 1-lb bunches?

____________

**2.** Another customer bought 6 bananas, 9 apples, and 1 pound of grapes. Based on the money he spent, identify an example of how he could purchase more fruit for less money.

____________

____________

____________

____________

____________

**3.** You have $10.00 to spend at Murphy's Fruit Stand. Give one example of how you could get the best value for the money. Tell what you would buy and how much money you would have left over.

____________

____________

____________

____________

____________